Cross-eyed Optimist

Cross-eyed Optimist

How I Learned to See in 3D and Straightened my Eyes with Vision Therapy

ROBERT BRYAN CROCKETT

novaheart
MEDIA

Halifax, Nova Scotia

Dedication

To my mother, Rev. Dr. Margaret Ellen Williams Crockett. Mom had the curiosity to delve into my condition, the courage to act, and the trust and candor to share what she knew. More than anything, though, she never gave up hope that someday I would see normally.

To my behavioral optometrist, Angela Dobson, whose courage to change her career made my transformation possible, and whose unfailing belief that I would succeed rightly earned her the name, "Pollyangela."

To Susan Barry, who described her experience in *Fixing My Gaze* and became the example I could follow.

To Gina Brown, my life partner, who supported me throughout the long transition, helped me to get my story out, comforted me when memories hurt, and still teaches me about love;

And
To all, especially children, who live with strabismus and to those who love them.

I don't want any strabismics or parents to deprive themselves or their loved ones of stereopsis. It is a true gift of sight!

Contents

Foreword ix

Introduction 3

1 1949 9

2 What Are the Odds? 10

3 My Early Years 13

4 Stereoblindness 18

5 My First All(eye)ance 21

6 My Father: "Eagle Eyes" 23

7 Early Ed 27

8 The Three Rs 31

9 Glasses (and Braces) 35

10 Mr. Godfrey's Class 37

11 Math and Physics 39

12 Sports 40

13 Hardware U 43

14 Eyes on the Road 47

15 Concord-Carlisle's Angry Young Man 49

16 Transcendental Revolutionary 52

17 Doctor My Eyes 54

18 Spinning Out of Academia 58

19	Aviation	60
20	An Arc of Boatbuilding	65
21	I Now See How I Saw	74
22	The Secret Society of Strabismics	79
23	"Stereo Sue"	81
24	Two Years on Hold	83
25	Vision Sense	85
26	The Road to 3D	89
27	Homework, Again	91
28	Mysterious Colored Lights	96
29	Neuroplasticity	99
30	Muscle Memories	101
31	Waiting to Pop	103
32	Reported Sightings	106
33	Finding the Switch	110
34	Vision Quest	115
35	Back to the Beginning	119
36	Broken Wings	121
37	Long Live the Wonder!	125
	In Hindsight	127
	What Vision Therapy Experts Say	129
	Acknowledgments	139
	Glossary	141
	Bibliography	147
	Resources	149
	Index	151

Foreword

On January 12, 2018, I was on a train bound for New York City when an email popped up on my smartphone. "I am now experiencing 3D vision which I can 'turn on' at will," the message read. After a few more lines, it was signed Buzz with a P.S. "I'll be seventy-two in May."

Buzz (Robert) Crockett and I had been corresponding by letter and email for several months when I received that email. He and I shared a common visual condition. We had been strabismic and stereoblind since early infancy. When we looked at an object, we did not direct both eyes toward that target as most people do. Instead, we aimed one eye at the object while turning away and suppressing the information from the other eye. But through vision therapy, we both learned to aim both eyes simultaneously at the same place in space and see in 3D. My story had been told first by Oliver Sacks in a 2006 article, titled "Stereo Sue" in *The New Yorker* and later by me in my book *Fixing My Gaze*. My experience, and Buzz's too, surprise many because they contradict a longstanding scientific theory that stereovision, the ability to see in 3D, can develop only during a "critical period" in early childhood. I was forty-eight when I began to see in 3D. Buzz was even older; he was seventy-one!

Two weeks after Buzz's first "stereo email," he sent me another:

Dear Susan,
For you, it was the snowflakes. For me it was passing over Halifax Harbor on the suspension bridge. I was enveloped in the cables, surprised and transfixed.
  And so many other discoveries...
  I'm writing things down. Maybe I can put some things together that can help others like you have.

And that's exactly what Buzz has done. He has written an engrossing and profound book, *Cross-eyed Optimist*, which is both a description of one man's life with strabismus and a statement about strabismus in general. In it, we follow Buzz's roller coaster childhood – his troubles learning to read in school, magical summer trips with his father even if he did not have the vision to appreciate the scenic views, his impulsive decision to drop out of college, and his career as a master boat builder. Buzz was nothing if not determined and rebellious. Although he was told that he could never fly a plane, he earned his pilot's license and spent a season flying taildraggers over the North Atlantic. With flying and with every other challenging task that Buzz chose to master, he found ways to adapt his compromised vision to what he wanted to do. Then, in his eighth decade, tired of finding ways to cope with his strabismus, he cured it.

Buzz did not transform his vision on his own. He worked with an exceptional optometrist, Dr. Angela Dobson, who after 20 years of work as a classical

optometrist, took a year off from her practice to learn
the science and tools behind behavioral optometry and
vision therapy. When Buzz began vision training with
Dr. Dobson, he balked at having to perform exercises
every day. He knew from his early failures in school that
he rebelled at having to practice. But he brought to his
therapy one great skill. What vision therapy teaches us is
how to abandon old, less useful habits and develop new
ones. We cannot abandon old habits, however, if we do not
know we have them. Since most of us develop perceptual
habits and skills early in life, we give them little thought,
if we are conscious of them at all. But Buzz knew he did
not see normally. Over and over again, he had adapted
his way of seeing to the skills he wanted to master. After a
lifetime of coping with his strabismus, Buzz was good at
watching himself see and of observing his mind at work.
Indeed, he taught the same self-awareness skills to his
clients when he became a life coach in his fifties. Now, he
brought those skills to his own vision therapy. He recalls,

"Even though I wasn't doing a lot of homework per se,
more of my attention each day was turned to the [vision
therapy] project. I simply began focusing on how much
of my vision was coming through my left (non-dominant)
eye... How much of the left lens of my glasses was I seeing
at the same time? My left upper and lower eyelids? The
left side of my nose? And was I still seeing the same on
the right?

"And I paid attention to what it took to make this
happen, to increase the vision in my left eye without
suppressing the right. Not surprisingly, the answer wasn't
doing something, but the opposite; it was to not do all

the things I did to suppress. I had to relax my face and not attempt to 'look' but to just 'see.' Angela called it 'looking softly.' This simple practice of getting my mind to erase a lifetime of ingrained behavior, is at the same time enormously profound. I was changing my brain with my mind, and persistence!"

What Buzz described, I see in every person I know who has substantially rehabilitated themselves: an intense awareness of how they take in the world and move through it.

In entertaining detail, Buzz describes the many exercises he performed in vision therapy and his frustration with them. But all his hard work paid dividends. Ten months after beginning therapy, Buzz happened to be cutting his fingernails when, to his astonishment, he experienced his first 3D view, that of an ordinary nail clipper. "It's hard to describe the thrill," he writes, "of having something transform in front of my eyes, to have something that had appeared one way all my life, now look different." That his view of something as mundane as nail clippers could bring out such wonder is a testament to the surprising power of first seeing with stereopsis. As Buzz gained greater control of his vision, colors became brighter and surfaces more textured. By balancing the input from his two eyes, his face, body, and gait became more symmetrical and balanced. He took a trip to the southwestern US in order to experience "Big Sky" country where he could now take in the entire vista from edge to edge. Above all, he realized that stereopsis provided much more than just a new view of the world. It provided a different feeling. "Stereoscopic vision," Buzz wrote, "to someone who has never experienced it, is more than seeing. With it comes a whole new feeling of having a world around me, of being included in it, and it being more alive and fluid." As he began to see the world in its fullness, he saw himself differently too. He no longer regarded himself as broken but felt himself as whole.

At the time Buzz began vision therapy, he was seventy years old and an accomplished pilot, boatbuilder, businessman, and life coach. Yet he regards his acquisition of stereopsis, his ability to change lifelong visual habits in his eighth decade, to be his greatest achievement. His story reminds us all that our brain remains plastic throughout life. The potential for transformation is always there, if only we can find the tools and motivation to unleash it.

Susan R. Barry

Professor Emeritus of Biology and Neuroscience, Mount Holyoke College

Author of *Fixing My Gaze: A Scientist's Journey into Seeing in Three Dimensions*

Cross-eyed Optimist

Introduction

I find myself saying today, to people I've known all my life, "I've never told you this, I've never told anyone this." I lived all my life with the shame and embarrassment of being "cross-eyed," and the trauma of multiple surgeries as an infant to "correct" my problem. Now I'm telling my story.

The sense of sight is one of the greatest gifts we have as human beings. We use it to learn about and find our way in the world, understand emotions and expressions, and even communicate with each other. Vision is complex and takes place in the brain, of which eyes are really components.

Human vision is all that much more wondrous because of our ability to see in three dimensions (3D). This is only possible when both eyes have learned to work together as a team, "fusing" their images in the brain to produce this amazing display.

The 96 or so percent of the population who are fortunate enough to have their eyes work together to produce 3D images mostly take this gift for granted and barely think about how complex and miraculous vision is.

For the other four percent who have strabismus, it's another story. I was one of those people, diagnosed with strabismus (crossed eyes) as an infant, and the impact of this diagnosis would ripple throughout my entire life, causing pain, continual eye problems and discomfort, lack of self-esteem, and much more.

My late mother wanted me to see like children with normal vision, and it was recommended to my parents that I have surgery on my eyes. In fact, I had two operations by the age of five that "straightened" my eyes, so that I no longer appeared cross-eyed. I remained stereoblind, however. My eyes hadn't learned to work together properly, so my brain essentially chose to view the world through one eye at a time, preferring that to confusion.

I am grateful that I wasn't teased for being cross-eyed, yet I have enormous compassion for those who are. The operations did not truly fix the problem, and deep inside I felt like I was broken. I couldn't see things properly or judge distance, nor could I catch a baseball or read very well. Although I was considered a bright student, school was very difficult.

I adapted, and life went on. It wasn't until I was 70 that I finally took active steps to address my strabismus, to learn to see in 3D. And I did that with vision therapy, a non-invasive treatment method that gets to the source of the problem: the brain, not the eyes or eye muscles.

Unfortunately, many eyecare professionals apparently still believe the eye muscles are the cause of strabismus. And strabismus surgeries continue to be performed despite the research, evidence, and proof that vision therapy can do more to help someone without the use of invasive surgery (see the bibliography and resources for information).

Vision is a complex process, and binocular vision involves the whole person, including the eyes. The eye muscles are very strong and are seldom the cause of strabismus (which also includes "wall-eye" and "lazy eye" conditions). Straightening the eyes with surgery only makes the brain's work more difficult, as evidenced by how the brain often turns the eye again soon after surgery.

Who Would Benefit from this Book?

Parents/Guardians
First, I wrote this book for parents of children who have vision challenges. Whether it's noticing something not working with your child's eyes, behavioral issues (possibly related to eye problems), or a physician diagnosing a medical condition, it is scary. Suddenly you are thrust into a new arena with many options presented and decisions to be made.

One of the scariest is being told your child needs surgery, even though there are no guarantees that the operation will straighten their eyes, and if it does, the straightening effect may be temporary. You may even be told by a surgeon that the muscles are fine, but an operation is still the only thing that can be done. As a result, some children have multiple surgeries that are traumatic, not only for children but for parents as well.

Further, even if the eyes are straightened because of the operation, a child may still suffer from any number of vision problems, including stereoblindness (not seeing in 3D). This is what happened to me after two operations as a child. And while my eyes appeared straight, I still suffered from the trauma of the operations and couldn't see in 3D. I couldn't read properly, focus, or retain what I had read. In school, they labeled me unmotivated, rebellious, and other terms that told me I was a problem. For a list of many symptoms and behaviors possibly linked to vision problems see the section What Vision Therapy Experts Say.

Adults

According to my optometrist, Dr. Dobson, many adult strabismics may not even be aware of their condition. Of those that are, some have had surgeries, often repeated several times, to align their eyes. Seldom do these surgeries result in stereoscopic (3D) vision. The traditional, and still prevalent, belief is that there is a "critical period" when the young brain is still plastic enough to achieve stereopsis (variously believed to be between two to ten years of age), and after that, it's too late. And while addressing problems at an early age is ideal, it's still possible to see in 3D at any age. I learned to see in 3D at 70!

Thanks to developments in vision therapy, we have learned that the critical period theory was never true – and more importantly, many eye problems can be corrected without surgery. Make no mistake, vision therapy is hard work. It can take months of continuous dedication to exercises and the use of specialty tools and equipment before noticeable changes occur. But the results are worth the effort.

Optometrists and Eye Specialists

Let me be clear, I am not a trained specialist and I'm not in a position to give medical advice. I am someone who had two surgeries that straightened my eyes, but it didn't correct my vision problems.

I lived with vision and eye issues my entire life – and mostly was told by optometrists that there was nothing that I could do. While I had heard of vision therapy as a young adult, I assumed it was only for very young children, and I didn't pursue it.

That was until I read the seminal article in *The New Yorker*, "Stereo Sue" by Dr. Oliver Sacks. He wrote of the success of Dr. Susan Barry, who learned to see in 3D at the age of 48, through vision therapy. It was the spark I needed to think that maybe I too could learn to see in 3D. That journey took another few years, but I've finally arrived.

I believe and hope you will consider that much of the trauma stemming from unnecessary surgeries could be eliminated by pursuing vision therapy instead. Since I am not a healthcare professional, I have listed resources and cited vision therapy professionals who have quietly pioneered a revolutionary solution that is achieved without operations, lifetime trauma, and pain.

This is my story – a 70-year journey starting with crossed eyes and living with (or ignoring) my eye challenges for a long, long time. Eventually, I realized that the trauma from the operations and my childhood sight problems had never gone away, that I had simply stored it in the cells of my body.

I wrote this book because I don't want others to go through what I, or my parents, did. Whether it's parents trying to deal with their young child going through one or more operations and the heartbreak of not fixing the problem, or especially the children, for having to go through multiple operations without understanding what is happening.

There are non-invasive methods to address a myriad of eye problems, and I would encourage every parent and strabismic to explore those possibilities first. Although I took the long, scenic route for decades, I finally learned to see in 3D and continue to this day. What a feeling!

1

1949

"Mommy, I'm blind," I whispered when I heard her voice.

No one had told me that both my eyes would be bandaged when I awoke, and I'd said nothing to the nurse. But when my mother arrived, my voice revealed my fear.

I was three when a surgeon first severed, then reattached, my eye muscles – and I had no idea what was happening. I'd been cross-eyed since infancy, and the operation was to line up my left eye with my right. I underwent a second operation two years later for the same reason.

I remember playing with a telephone truck in my bed. I loved that truck, and to this day I remember its color, details, and the way I felt when I played with it. That, my sole memory of the time, was probably my second operation at five. Until recently, I thought it was my only memory.

What Are the Odds?

When I came into this world, my eyes were like most newborns. In the delivery room, they saw brightness, color and motion. Yet my vision was out of focus, vague, and confusing.

My eyes would have responded to light, color, and motion, rotating freely, erratically, and somewhat independently. Like every other muscle in my newborn body, my eye muscles were uncoordinated. They had yet to develop communication with my brain through the training of neurons to form pathways.

Within a few weeks or months, about 95 to 96 percent of infants' eyes "find each other" and merge their images in the brain, referred to as "fusion."[1] This normal, binocular vision strengthens as the muscles that control each eyeball learn to automatically coordinate so they can converge to see the end of one's nose or diverge to look at the horizon. The brain not only knows how to converge, or bring the eyes together, to focus on a near object; extraordinarily, it also learns to judge distance from this convergence.

As days and weeks progressed, I began to control my eyes, much as I learned to bring my other muscles, small

---

1   Susan Barry, *Fixing My Gaze: A Scientist's Journey into Seeing in Three Dimensions*, (New York: Basic Books, 2010), 18.

and large, under control. I reached for things with my hands and I followed them with my eyes. Yet my eyes didn't discover the best way to work together.

Because my eyes didn't fuse and team up neurologically, I must have seen two of everything. My eyes, two independent points of view streaming to my brain were in conflict with my sense of touch. Long before I was aware, my brain relied on touch to confirm there was only one object when my eyes saw two. My brain set about adapting to this conflict by doing all it could to get rid of the second image that it knew didn't belong.

My right eye became dominant and my left eye was suppressed. The most obvious sign was that my left eye turned toward my nose. My eyes crossed in an effort to minimize the confusion (as I appear on the cover of this book).

Infantile strabismus, as this is called, most often appears as crossed eyes. The eyes may also turn out, up or down. Suppression can also include weakening of the non-dominant eye. Often there is no eye turn, but vision can be impaired beyond correction with lenses, a strabismic condition called amblyopia. Strabismus can also appear later in life, from trauma or disease.

My left eye didn't keep up with its dominant counterpart. It became more near-sighted and astigmatic, and it didn't open as much. The suppression went much further than my eyes and had profound effects on my entire body, something I wouldn't discover for decades.

My right eye is dominant, but unlike some strabismics, I could see with either one eye or the other. I have always alternated between which eye I was "looking through." This happens involuntarily when my left eye has a better view, but I could also choose an eye. I can sight a telescope or rifle without closing the other eye. Doctors told my mom I had "monocular vision," and that I was an "alternator."

My Early Years

I was conceived when my Dad returned from the war in the Pacific.

Jim Crockett was the rare individual who knew his passion from his earliest childhood: flowers. Encouraged in the garden as a toddler by my grandmother, by the time he met my Mom, he was already preparing his professor's classes for him at Texas A&M. He was quiet and he was strong, having worked in plant nurseries throughout his youth in New England.

My mother, Margaret Ellen Williams, was a recent graduate of Rice University in Houston, Texas, when she met Jim. The first woman to receive a full scholarship at the school, she had finished with honors in English. Mom was strong as well as smart and remained fit and sharp throughout her life.

When I was not yet born, and my sister still an infant in arms, my parents drove their meager belongings from San Francisco to New England, which had the plant-growing climate my Dad sought. Carol and I were years away from kindergarten, but my parents chose Concord, Massachusetts because of its schools, and we moved into a little red house on Old Bedford Road, just inside the town line. Dad opened a flower shop in nearby Lexington.

Mom and Dad had few means, but they clearly loved and cared for their children. When my eyes crossed in my infancy, they naturally sought the best advice from doctors. The advice then, and to a large extent today, was surgery. The doctors proposed to straighten my eyes by severing and repositioning muscles on my eyeballs.

The first surgery didn't achieve the desired results and was repeated two years later. That was in 1949 and 1951 when I was three and five.

Strabismus surgery was already 150 years old; the procedure hadn't changed since 1922[2] and it wouldn't change again until 1970. The entire premise behind strabismic surgery has a false basis. A growing minority of well-informed eye doctors are proving that fact. Severing eye muscles and reconnecting them elsewhere on the eyeball surely is based upon the belief that it's the muscles that are the problem, not the brain. I now believe it's the other way around and that's why reoperations are so prevalent.[3]

When my bandages came off, my brain saw double again and repeated its previous behavior, turning my left eye back toward my nose. My brain taking charge of my eye necessitated my second surgery. I now understand that our eye muscles are much stronger than they need to be, strong enough to overcome anything a surgeon might do.

---

2 C. Remy, and P. Aracil, "History of Strabismus Surgery," *Journal francais d'ophthamologie*, 1984. Available: National Institute of Health, National Library of Medicine. www.pubmed.gov.

3 Steven Gallop, *A Parent Guide to Strabismus, Eye Muscle Surgery & Vision Therapy* (Santa Ana: Optometric Extension Foundation Program, 2014), 65–66.

My brain must have given up the fight after two surgeries, and did not turn my eye appreciably again. Strabismus surgeries, mostly performed on children, are repeated multiple times in some cases, mostly unnecessarily, and on a scale I find painful to imagine.[4] Not only children are traumatized by this experience, but parents as well. My mother never gave up the wish that I would see normally and always felt guilty that she hadn't been able to do more to help me, as I recently learned from a sister.

Like most who endure strabismus surgery at a young age, I have carried the trauma all my life. I hope that my story might encourage parents to consider an alternative. Just writing that sentence touched those scars enough to make me sob.

For as long as surgery has been around, a few eye doctors have tried non-invasive methods of helping strabismics with some success, especially in young children. Their field is referred to as vision therapy or vision training, which includes corrective lenses, specialist tools, and a vast array of vision exercises.

Surgery was and still is the norm (for more on why this is the case, see In Hindsight section). Most eye doctors are introduced to vision therapy in their studies, but it may not be emphasized. They learn little about its efficacy, or worse, choose to ignore it. Unfortunately, the livelihoods of many ophthalmologists rely on the sole practice of strabismus surgery.

---

4   According to Optometrists Network, "Most children under the age of 10 will need multiple procedures to obtain optimal results." https://www.optometrists.org/a-guide-to-eye-turns/ strabismus-crossed-eyes/strabismus-surgery/

Doctors who practice vision therapy, however, know its power. They know that in most cases surgery is not required to not only straighten the eyes, but to get them working together. My parents certainly weren't aware of that in 1949 and 1951, and the vast majority of North American eye doctors still don't know it today. I received no vision therapy after my surgery.

After two surgeries, my strabismus wasn't obvious to someone looking at me. According to Dr. Pilar Vergara Giménez, an eye turn of less than 12–15 degrees isn't usually noticeable.[5] My left eye still turned in and up a few degrees and was rotated, and I was still stereoblind.

However, I've had many experiences of looking at, and speaking to, someone in a group only to have them look over their shoulder to see if I was talking to someone else, or to have the person next to them answer me. I became very self-conscious when speaking in a group. I would do whatever I could to avoid the situation. Eventually, when introduced to a group of people, I developed the skill of learning everyone's name quickly, so that I could speak to them by name and not rely on my eyes to address them.

What appearance didn't reveal was that my eyes still operated as they had before – independently. As mentioned earlier, my parents were told that I had alternating, "monocular" vision. It's been believed for some time that fusion in infantile strabismus could not be

---

5   Pilar Vergara Giménez, *Crossed & Lazy Eyes: Myths, Misconceptions and Truths* (Timonium, Maryland: Optometric Extension Program Foundation, Inc., 2016), 37–38.

achieved after about the age of five. And what would come to be called the "critical period" was closing.[6]

Interestingly, it's also the age at which we begin storing permanent memories. I entered that period with certain knowledge of one thing: There was something wrong with me, some defect that my parents had tried to "fix," but they were only partly successful. How that fact would impact my life was about to unfold.

---

6   Correspondence with Susan Barry, December, 2020.

4

Stereoblindness

I was told that I had monocular vision and I'd always
thought of my condition in those terms, despite an
obvious paradox: I'd always had peripheral vision in both
eyes, all the time! Doctor Robin Lewis, whom I came to
know on this journey, brought this fact to my attention.
My vision has always been binocular, just not optimal.
Stereoblindness is a better term, because neither eye
was blind; I was simply blind to stereoscopic (3D) vision
and stereopsis. I learned that everyone with two eyes
has binocular vision. In my case, as well as that of other
strabismics, our brains arranged our eyes to work together,
but not as well as they could.

Robin Lewis describes stereopsis this way: "[It] is the
awareness of the fullness of the volume of space within
which you live and understanding the relationships
of everything within it. It is more than seeing in 3D.
It is dynamic. It is more like living in 3D, being able
to anticipate changes in relationship and to manage
both how those changes occur and your response to a
changing environment."

For all my life, I had no idea of what 3D vision would
be like, or that there was anything like stereopsis. They
were beyond my conception. And I believed 3D vision was
unattainable anyway.

Beyond the embarrassment of not being able to look someone in the eye and having an obvious impairment, and the emotional pain of appearing cross-eyed or wall-eyed, or having a "lazy eye," stereoblindness is inferior to stereoscopic vision in several ways.

Another term that I used incorrectly my entire life because I had no experience of 3D vision or stereopsis, was depth perception. In my 2D world, it only meant "distance perception," how far away something was on a line-of-sight, not "the awareness of the fullness of the volume…"

Distance perception within a few feet is greatly affected by stereoblindness. When two eyes are focused together on a nearby object, the brain uses geometry to determine distance visually. The eyes will converge when that object moves closer. A stereoptic person focused on the end of a pen at arm's length will cross their eyes a little to do so, and more as they move the pen towards their nose.

Because the two eyes are apart, the stereoptic person's brain can discern the angle between them and translate that into a sense of distance. This sense is important to species that hunt. That's why their eyes are on the front of their faces. Your cat knows just how far away the mouse lies.

Measuring distance by geometry, whether to a distant planet or an incoming baseball, requires two points of observation. In the distance that I could reach with a baseball bat, a golf club, or a hammer, stereoblindness greatly impaired my distance perception. Other clues, such as perspective and motion parallax, provide little distance information within a few feet, where our brain's ability to compute the geometry is so valuable.

I knew that I was missing something called 3D vision, of which I had no experience. I would describe what I saw as flat, but it wasn't that exactly. And while I always had peripheral vision simultaneously with both eyes, my brain filtered out duplicate images from one eye, usually my left. It is extraordinary that my brain could so effectively block out most of the field of vision of one eye or the other, with only an occasional double image slipping through. What an enormous amount of brain power it must take and how taxing it must be, compared to simply fusing two similar images into 3D vision.

As an example, my parents gave me a View-Master, a stereoscope toy, one Christmas. While others enjoyed 3D images of all kinds of things, I saw a single, tiny, square, flat transparency through either eye. I had no way to understand what my three sisters saw, but I never said a word, except "thank you."

Our eyes are on the front of our faces; we are forward looking – and that's where, right in the middle – the battle between my eyes took place. I never understood until now how much I was missing because of that "battle for the middle." I was missing any sense of the panorama, the wholeness of the space around me. I also had a sense of not being whole myself.

My First All(eye)ance

If my mother had failed to warn me before my first surgery that I wouldn't be able to see when I awoke, she made up for it from then onward by sharing all she knew about my condition. She learned all she could about it and encouraged me to do the same. I was in grade five when she suggested I dissect a cow's eye for my science project and made arrangements with the local butcher. My most vivid memory is not visual, but the smell of formaldehyde. The cow's eye was impressive nonetheless, and I got a chance to see the inside workings of an eye while grossing out some of my classmates.

Mom was highly intelligent and extremely logical (in fact, she taught me both classical logic and sentence diagramming as a child). She was also religious and in later life would earn her master's from Harvard Divinity School and her doctorate from Andover Newton. She helped others through ministry and counseling into her 90s. When it came to my condition, although she understood the science, she always hoped for a miracle.

Mom understood my vision affected what we called "depth perception." She understood that the critical period for stereopsis to occur had passed. She explained why I had trouble hitting or catching a baseball, and why I would never be able to fly an airplane. Despite that, she never lost hope that I would someday see in 3D.

One of my earliest and most vivid memories, one that felt important at the time and still does, was about Mom. I was about eight and I was waiting for her in the children's room of the Concord Library. I remember coming to the very clear conclusion that I could always rely on my mother. Simple as that. And I was right.

My Father: "Eagle Eyes"

My father could read a road sign before we even knew there was one, and it seemed he could stand in any field, look down, and pick out a four-leaf clover whenever he wanted. He could also pick out any tree, shrub, flower or weed, tell you its common and botanical names and a lot more about it. At the age of four he had known that flowers would be his life's love.

Dad had worked as a nurseryman and had a laborer's hands and arms. He was at Pearl Harbor and in the South Pacific during the war, and I understand that very few shipmates beat him at arm wrestling. My father was sober and married, so when ashore, he used every opportunity to add to his botanical knowledge. He collected leaves and flowers from each island he visited, pressing them between the pages of books aboard ship and documenting each specimen. These are now museum items, though each description had its location neatly excised by the wartime censors.

After the opening of his flower shop, he immediately began writing an eight-page pamphlet on the care of flowers for his customers. Printed with green ink, it was small enough to slip in a pocket, an invoice, or suitable deliveries. On the cover, above the imprint "Crockett's Flowers," was the pamphlet's name in script, *Flowery*

Talks. Dad loved flowers so much that he just wanted to share his knowledge with others. He became a pioneer in educational advertising, an "infopreneur."

He soon sold his successful shop and went on the road, selling *Flowery Talks* to florists in all 48 states of the US. Every town large enough to have a flower shop was a target. Monthly, the florist would receive the number of pamphlets they had ordered, each with their shop's imprint on the cover. Each shop was visited annually for the renewal. This was a lot of territory to cover, and soon Dad's mother and father were on the road selling *Flowery Talks*, followed by Dad's college roommate and his wife.

Dad must have been sympathetic to my plight as the only boy among three girls, and twice during my youth, he brought me along on sales trips, just the two of us! The first trip, when I was seven, was to the southeastern states. We traveled to New York City and Washington, D.C., where we visited the White House and even went to a church service with the President, Dwight Eisenhower. Dad pointed to him in the congregation below us, but I couldn't pick him out of the crowd.

The big trip was the summer I was nine. We spent three months visiting every town with a flower shop west of El Paso, Texas and the Prairies. I spent hours alone in the car while he made sales calls, long and short. The waiting was more than made up for by the hours that I spent with Dad, listening to Art Linkletter, Arthur Godfrey, or Sergeant Preston of the Yukon on the radio, talking or taking in the view. We stopped often to take photos of each other in front of signs or at roadside lookoffs. It amazed me at how others found such views so satisfying.

The bigger the view, the more I was aware that it didn't fit together quite right. Once in a while we'd get a nickel Coke and a bag of Fritos or treat ourselves to a soft ice cream. I didn't bring toys on the trip, but there was a simple hand air pump that I played with upside down, with my feet on the handles. I held the bottom end like it was the controls of an airplane, and I spent endless hours in the back seat, climbing, diving, banking and flying my imaginary plane. That was a magical summer.

It wouldn't always be that way. Puberty came between my father and me like a wall. For years, when I thought about it, I presumed that he hated me, and I him. We stretched the generation gap, and I did my best to make it sting all around whenever it snapped back. Which it did.

When I wasn't under his skin, Dad was mild-mannered and unassuming. Yet he could read a person's eyes and identify the dishonest ones. He called them "shifty-eyed." I never asked him if he thought my eyes were shifty. They seemed that way to me. When he spoke of not trusting people who couldn't look you straight in the eyes, I felt that included me. I don't think it ever occurred to him that his words hurt me, and I never mentioned it to him. Dad's comments weren't the sole reason for my lack of confidence in face-to-face encounters with others. But my eyes were at the center of it.

I now realize Dad's strict and difficult childhood made it hard for him to express emotions like love or even empathy. Despite the pain I felt, I probably sensed even then what I know for certain now, that he always deeply loved me. He taught me character, and that lying was cheating at life.

That is how I remember my parents in my childhood. I had broken eyes that they hadn't been able to fix, that didn't work anywhere near like my father's, and that might even be "shifty."

7

Early Ed

I began kindergarten at the Alcott School. It's probably no accident that school begins about the time that we become capable of laying down permanent memories. We moved that year to a new house my father and grandfather had built closer to the center of Concord. I retain very few memories of Old Bedford Road and the period of my surgeries. Conscious memories, that is. I can remember the pain of my school years, however.

Thus, with a few tears from a five-year-old on my first day, I began a 13-year ordeal in Concord public schools. In that crucible my vision would now challenge me in every way: the classroom, sports, and social life.

And let me be clear: my eyes appeared to be normal following the two surgeries. They didn't work though; I couldn't always aim my eyes so that someone knew I was looking at them. I was embarrassed and ashamed. Nonetheless, I've always been grateful to my parents for arranging what they called "cosmetic surgery." They knew of no alternatives. As much as I suffered from my impaired vision, it's hard for me to imagine the life of a noticeably cross-eyed child.

I wonder how other children at my school felt. Did they feel like insiders or outsiders? Or did they even think about it? From that first day of kindergarten and throughout my entire life, I felt like I didn't know how things worked in this world like others seemed to, and I didn't feel like I fit in. Yet I never shared these thoughts, or the feeling that I was broken and couldn't be fixed.

Which came first? The strabismus or the introversion? Who knows? Few acquaintances know I'm an introvert. They assume that when I'm not being cheerful and energetic around them, I'm doing it with someone else, rather than spending hours and days alone.

School forces introverts to endure six to seven hours every day, five days a week, without a moment alone. Much of the time I spent in school, my mind wanted to be elsewhere, and often was. It's definitely an environment better suited to extroverts, but who thinks about that? Especially me, then. I better understand introversion now and am comfortable calling myself one, but I still wonder if I was always an introvert, or was I shaped by my strabismic life?

What makes an introvert draw attention to himself, as I did? I was often what others called the "class clown." I never referred to myself that way; the expression embarrassed me somehow. There might have been lots of reasons for my behavior. I wasn't confident about my looks, nor was I athletic, but I was smart and quick, and this way I felt they would notice me. I didn't want to be noticed for my eyes or my vision.

The chalkboard was the focus of the classroom, and one of the teacher's two principal tools, the other being her voice. Later, she added books, but I always learned more by listening than by looking. Wherever I sat in the classroom, or however I held the book, making sense of what my eyes saw was never easy. A consequence of the surgery is that my left eye no longer looked at my nose, but straight ahead, increasing the suppression load on my brain. My right eye dominated, while what my left sent to my brain still lurked in the "middle." It was easier to find any distraction than to focus with my eyes.

As I write today, 70 years later, my understanding of *how* I saw is much greater than it was then. At the same time, I want to share the feelings I had as a strabismic boy at the Alcott School from kindergarten to fifth grade.

First off, my eyes weren't able to work together by "fusing" on an object, say, and creating a 3D image in the brain, the way normal eyes work. I could alternate between my eyes, using whichever gave me the best point of view at that moment. My right eye, however, was dominant and took over most of the time. It was nearly 20/20 compared to my left eye, which was both myopic (nearsighted) and astigmatic (think: twisted vision), as well as turned up slightly and toward my nose. I know now it was not easily noticed, yet I lived in constant fear of being found out. I never wore glasses in school, for reasons I will discuss later.

I've mentioned before that I've always had simultaneous peripheral vision, both left and right. My brain had no trouble dealing with the image from my left eye that was out of range of my right, or vice versa. Besides, the vision on the edges is fuzzy anyway.

Both eyes are continuously live-streaming complete images to my brain. Because it cannot fuse these images, my brain somehow suppresses most of the stream from one eye. The suppressed visual information is coming from the very place I'm looking: *right in front of me,* where the potential for clear vision with either eye would have been the greatest! The battle for the middle wasn't limited to chalkboards; it would be the same with books, but up close. And the closer I was looking, the more it seemed that my left eye was in the way.

School was more difficult for me than for others, but some had it worse, and I adapted. I listened and remembered, even when I was clowning around. I had one good eye and two good ears, and used them proportionately to learn. Despite the challenges, I loved learning.

8

The Three Rs

Of the "Three Rs," reading has been the most paradoxical, writing has been the hardest while the most rewarding, and arithmetic has been the easiest. Being *in* the classroom has always been difficult. I would have rather been elsewhere.

Reading I can best describe as a "push" versus "pull" paradox. From my earliest childhood, I have found it extremely difficult to read anything that was required. It was not even rebellion against authority. If I had to "push" my eyes to read anything, my brain found it difficult to suppress the image from my left eye, confusing me. I might have to read a sentence, paragraph, or page several times to get the meaning. Sometimes when I was tired, reading would become so difficult, I would cover one eye with my hand. I didn't enjoy doing this, though, because it made the world appear smaller.

And maybe it's because my left eye was suppressed, but I often had a difficult time finding the next line on the page, as my eyes moved from the right, back to the left. As if I were looking into a blind spot, my eye would skip a line. Only when the sentence no longer made sense would I go back to find my place. I hated reading assignments and would do anything to avoid them.

"Pull" reading was entirely different, such as the magazine article that caught my eye when I was setting the table or taking out the garbage. It was the reading I did every single night until I was supposed to be asleep, and then long after. I loved stories of all kinds, especially tales of the sea. When I realized my parents could hear the click of my bed lamp going off as they climbed the stairs to check that we were asleep, I began to turn the light out by silently unscrewing the bulb. Neither parent ever thought to check the lamp's temperature in all those years!

But why the difference? When interest drove me to read, it was like my eyes were pulled along without a problem. At night, for example, I would read until I couldn't keep my eyes open. Yet when it was something I was assigned to read, or even something I wanted to read but didn't find interesting, my eyes got in the way of each other. They weren't being pulled along. This reading paradox remained my entire life. To me, this is more evidence that vision takes place in the brain.

Writing is the other side of reading, and good writing requires a lot of reading. I grew up around writing. Besides *Flowery Talks*, my Dad wrote several books, including the Time-Life Encyclopedia of Gardening. I witnessed the incredible amount of reading that his work entailed.

I credit my Mom with my love of words. She told me about the Roman and Greek roots of our language, and she taught me the clarity of proper prose. I collected words like other kids collected baseball cards. I grew my vocabulary for the sheer joy of learning. Words came easily for me but writing required too much "push" reading! Writing, therefore, became an activity I avoided.

Mathematics was my strength. It was precise and rational. It required some reading, for sure, but much was conceptual. For as long as I can remember, right up to the present, I've enjoyed doing math in my head. No vision required!

Except for sixth grade, I had always been streamed with the brightest kids. My grade five teacher may have mistaken my vision problems for low intelligence. For grade six, they placed me with the "slowest" kids. We got along just fine, and I formed friendships that lasted through high school.

Through grade six, classwork was all we had. I learned quickly and was bored much of the time, dreaming of the outdoors, or simply daydreaming. With junior high and high school came homework. Homework was anathema! Homework required *focus*. Homework required the carrying of books (book bags were unheard of) and I wanted my hands free. And *freedom* had always been my be-all and end-all. Homework definitely felt like PUSH to me!

Educators knew very little in the 1950s and 60s about learning challenges in general, and vision problems in particular. Although I went to one of the best public schools in America at the time, I don't believe there was ever a discussion with my educators about my visual challenges, how they may be dealt with, and the behaviors that might arise. Back then, public schools lacked the evaluation tools that exist today, and some terms that were used to describe my learning challenges and behavior would no longer be tolerated.

Today, children are diagnosed with ADD, ADHD, dyslexia, "acting out" and others – when in fact, those behavioral symptoms may be caused by vision problems and may disappear when solved. (See Section: Signs, Symptoms and Behaviors Resulting from Vision Problems) Throughout my life I've shown symptoms attributed to both ADD and dyslexia, including the avoidance of up-close tasks and reversals of letters, words and numbers in both reading and writing. While the latter happens rarely, it does happen. I was never professionally tested for these conditions, yet I exhibited many of the symptoms throughout my life and they may have been associated with my vision problems.

Ideally, to my mind, children should be screened early for visual acuity and also for binocular vision disorders, by a trained specialist. Even children fitted with glasses may have undetected issues. Neuroplasticity is greater in youth, so why delay treatment?

9

Glasses (and Braces)

I got my first bike at seven and my first eyeglasses after that. I don't know why it took so long. Vision with my left eye was obviously much poorer than my right, which was almost 20/20, but who wants glasses at any age?

When I did get glasses, I never wore them, except under the scrutiny of my parents. Every morning, as I headed off to the school bus, I would stash them in the tool shed along the way and every evening I would retrieve them as I returned home.

Sure, I was vain and didn't want four eyes. More importantly, I didn't like the way I saw with glasses on. The glasses improved my left eye acuity, but by doing so, made things worse. In order to suppress my left eye, my brain had originally turned it toward my nose and weakened its acuity. My brain arranged all of that in order to reduce the confusion.

Straightening my eyes with surgery made my brain's job harder again because instead of looking at my nose, my left eye was looking at almost the same place as my right. By improving the acuity of my left eye with glasses, I was only further reversing my brain's previous work. Seeing clearly with both eyes just made things more confusing. Intuitively, I understood this, but didn't talk about it. I just knew that I didn't like wearing them, even at home when nobody was looking. I would not wear glasses until my thirties.

My pattern of hiding appliances continued when our dentist recommended that I needed braces to push out my upper teeth. The braces weren't visible, as they were clasped to my rear molars, but they were uncomfortable as hell and in less than a week I discovered how to unclasp and remove them. They were also stashed and only taken out for visits to the dentist.

After a suitable number of visits, the dentist declared the work a success and removed the bands from my molars. I never said a word to my parents about hiding my braces or that the dentist was a fraud.

10

Mr. Godfrey's Class

Junior high was in a different school and I was back with the accelerated group of students. Grades seven and eight were the last times I even attempted to play ball games at recess with my vision challenges. I enjoyed learning, but I avoided reading and homework. So far, my vision wasn't affecting my marks because I excelled at tests by listening carefully in class. It frustrated me how much time was spent to learn so little. One exception was Mr. Godfrey's class.

Leonard Godfrey taught social studies to our group both years. The classroom was specially outfitted for an experiment in which we were the subjects. Microphones hung from wires strung over the tables where we sat. And looming above us was the one-way mirror of the viewing room. That was Dr. Oliver's domain. His perfectly bald pate and absolute silence added to the mystery of his lair. All we knew was that he was from Harvard observing us while we were learning about critical thinking.

Mr. Godfrey was Dr. Oliver's opposite. He was big, gruff, and had the history to back up his demeanor. He had been part of the Manhattan project assembled to deliver the atomic bomb to Japan. Godfrey was the navigator on the B-29 bomber *Great Artiste* when the second atomic bomb was dropped on Nagasaki on Aug 9, 1945. The plane he was in didn't drop the bomb, but he showed us photos he had taken of the mushroom cloud. This was the late '50s, and although almost 100,000 Japanese were killed and injured that day, it was believed that the A-bombs helped end the war and bring people like my father home.

Critical thinking fascinated me and fit with my single-eyed view of the world. I saw things differently than most people, and my personality took shape around this. I would learn the difference between claims and facts and to identify loaded statements and value judgements. It would forever frustrate me that others hadn't gained this discernment, especially my father.

Math and Physics

Our high school had some of the best teachers anywhere, and among them were Tom Dillon, who taught physics, and Norton Levy, who taught math, known as "Matt" and "Jug" to the students. I respected them both.

I loved the precision of mathematics and its use in physics. I remember a quote on Mr. Levy's wall, referring to mathematics as the "eyes of science."

As I examine the choices I made and the interests I pursued, they were influenced by the limitations placed on me by my vision. But were there also advantages in having a singular point of view? Does a brain that's learned to handle images of the outside world one eye at a time process other things differently, too? I'd revisit these questions throughout my life.

Sports

I feel like a phony even writing the word "sports." Why should I? Is that bad sportsmanship? I know nothing of sports. I have no interest in sports. Yet, as I reflect on it, there was a short time when I wanted to play sports and even enjoyed them.

Brief memories remain of playing hockey on the pond or baseball or touch football in someone's yard. Organized sports, even at the earliest age, spoiled that for me. I didn't like being the last picked for a team, and I knew why. Why would they want me? I'd only let the team down.

I couldn't hit and I couldn't catch. And I once broke an opponent's arm when I ran into him on the ice. I wasn't checking; I just hadn't seen him.

As much as the close-up effects of strabismus discouraged my interest in playing sports, distance vision spoiled spectator sports as well. Despite good visual acuity in my right eye, the confusion of the battle for the middle seemed to block my view. I remember watching the baseball great, Ted Williams, playing at Fenway Park, but I don't remember seeing anything.

By high school I had given up any interest in sports and stopped attending most games. Sports seemed to consume the lives of my male classmates, however. Not only the sports they played at gym and after school, but the professional teams that they followed through the seasons. I didn't even speak their language.

To be fair, there was no talk of sports at home, as I now realize there must have been for so many other kids. Their dads read about their teams in the papers and followed games on the radio, and then television. I only remember playing catch with Dad once or twice. His mitt looked like it came out of a museum, and my catching didn't improve, nor did my feeling of not belonging.

Stereoblindness greatly affected my ability to play sports that required hand-eye coordination, eye coordination in general, and balance. Poor distance perception was a big factor. I couldn't tell how far away the ball was, how fast it was coming or where it would be next. To make matters worse, I now realize that at the very instant I had to catch the ball or connect the bat, my vision would, in an instant, change from one eye to the other, and possibly back, missing the action altogether.

Like many kids with vision problems, I was regarded as uncoordinated, and to some extent, my vision made me so. In part it was because I never had a full field of vision and never fully trusted what I saw. I later learned the broad effects on my entire body, of my brain's effort to suppress the images from one eye. This, and our reliance on vision for balance, were additional challenges in sports.

During grade school recesses, kids tossed baseballs and footballs, and in the beginning, I tried to participate. In gym class when we chose teams, I was always one of the last to be chosen, and, in dodgeball, I was one of the first eliminated because frankly, I didn't see it coming.

As much as sports seemed to bring joy to other boys, they made me feel inadequate and isolated. Nobody wanted me on their team, and lacking their common interest and experiences, I felt left out socially as well.

My vision limited my interest in sports, but I've always walked. I walked a lot, and mostly alone.

Saturdays were the toughest, the loneliest. Summer days, too, but on Saturdays there was always something going on. And I wasn't part of it – probably didn't even know what it might be. I felt left out. So, I walked – always alone – on sidewalks, along country roads and woodland paths, I walked for hours.

Later, in my youth, I hitchhiked. And while I waited for a ride, I walked. I estimate that I hitchhiked the length of the Equator, crisscrossing North America six times and from Northern British Columbia, Canada to Acapulco, Mexico. In that time, I must have walked several thousand miles.

Maybe it's because of the solace walking gave me then that I enjoy it now. When I walk alone now, I'm grateful for the solitude (and more recently for the opportunity to focus on my vision). Recently, while "taking my eyes for a walk," the feelings I had as a boy, pacing out my solitary life, suddenly rushed over me again.

13

Hardware U

Sports filled the afternoons and Saturdays of most of my classmates. I mowed lawns in summer and shoveled snow in winter. I'd envied the older boys in their green cotton blazers arriving at Mrs. Hamm's house with deliveries in Vanderhoof Hardware's green truck, while I was cutting the grass. I was three months shy of my sixteenth birthday before I got up the nerve to apply for a job at the store. It overjoyed me when I received a call from Parker Vanderhoof that evening telling me I had the job.

Every afternoon, I'd go from our new high school where the town dump once smoked, to Vanderhoof's store on the Milldam, Concord's tiny center. Featured in a *Reader's Digest* article years later as "Hardware U," this multi-generational shop became my second home and its denizens, my other family. Parker, the founder's grandson, managed the store and was my boss. Responsibility had given him a maturity beyond his 32 years. Looking back, he was one of the best bosses I've ever had, always in good humor, encouraging and never making me feel wrong.

Phil Vanderhoof, 70, still came to the store most days and often brought his wife. They both knew the merchandise and customers as well as anyone. He always wore a three-piece suit and she a dress. I always addressed them as Mr. and Mrs. Vanderhoof. Phil taught me how to sharpen scissors, cut glass, and develop a signature that I could always deny was mine. Why he taught me that last one, I don't know, as I always found him to be scrupulously honest. It was a rare pleasure to go to his home for as mundane a chore as shoveling coal for his antiquated furnace.

Mrs. Nelson, the bookkeeper, was seldom seen but missed nothing as she lurked in her tiny alcove. And then there was Reggie, a traumatic brain injury survivor and jokester, the only other full-time clerk.

I have had a compassion for, and become friends with, brain-injured people throughout my life. But Reggie was the first. He was a great storyteller, full of anecdotes, all of which had at least a grain of truth. Reggie also knew lots of ribald rhymes and lewd expressions, welcome fodder for a 16-year-old building a vocabulary.

I was a willing worker, eager to learn, and Reggie may have taken advantage of this. Reggie was building a house for himself and his wife in a nearby town, and I devoted a lot of time one summer to helping him after work and on weekends. I enjoyed learning about house construction, being active outdoors and getting to drive the flat-bed truck from time to time. There was a vague promise of payment, which I don't think even I believed.

I loved wearing the green Vanderhoof jacket. Here I could smoke cigarettes and share stories in back with the others when we knew that the older folks were out of earshot. And I could hone my sales skills in one-on-one encounters with customers. Phil had pointed out to me that everybody entering the store was working on some project. That intrigued me. I took great pleasure in confidently telling people how to use our products, many of which I hadn't used myself.

Throughout my life, finding anything on a store shelf has been exasperating and depressing due to stereoblindness. At Vanderhoof's my vision wasn't a handicap. I knew where all 30,000 items were because I stocked the shelves.

At any other time, being asked to go find something, especially in a store, has triggered immediate stress. It helps if I know exactly what the item I am seeking looks like, and I'm thrown off further if it looks different. Faced with a wall of shelves, my brain seems unable to scan each one in the way most people do. Maybe it's the battle for the middle. In any case, my usual difficulty and reluctance to read seems worse when faced with a wall of labels – it's frustrating and there's too much stimulation. I'm not able to take in everything intelligibly, and as a result, I become overwhelmed. And undoubtedly, the memory of past failures starts me out on edge. I'm more aware now of this lifelong challenge and its connection with my vision.

I'm sure that keeping my vision problems a secret added to the stress of finding things. I never revealed my condition to people outside my family for the simple reason that I didn't want to show my weakness. Instead, rather than ask for help, I endured the feeling of shame. Whether I took a very long time to find something in a store, or someone had to point it out to me, the embarrassment remained. It wasn't limited to finding things in stores, either. I loved the idea of fetching things for my father when I was young, yet from the moment he asked me, I'd be afraid of failing. Too often he'd have to get it himself, in plain view, or admonish me to "look harder" which only made it worse. Thinking back, I developed quite a phobia about being asked to find things. In a retail shop, I always look for a clerk before I look for an item.

At Vanderhoof's in my teens, I hadn't figured all of this out about my vision. I just knew that I met people close-up, one-on-one, where I was most comfortable, and we spoke of practical matters. It was a refuge from the academic and social challenges at school and the pressures at home.

Vanderhoof's was my hangout, and it was also my means to pay for my freedom, which came in the form of a car and the money to operate it. I was three months short of my sixteenth birthday when I started work there, and the freedom that a driver's license would bestow occupied my dreams.

14

Eyes on the Road

Vision issues arose again as my sixteenth birthday approached, and I worried if I might have problems with the eye tests for my driver's license. Again, stereoblindness didn't seem to be an issue, but acuity was. My license required me to wear glasses when driving, though for the life of me, I cannot recall wearing them. My driving test was more challenging because I was wearing unfamiliar eyeglasses.

I must have kept my glasses nearby in case the police stopped me, but from my perspective, they were more of an impairment to my vision than an aid. Improved acuity from the glasses interfered with my left eye suppression, making it harder for my brain to interpret information from my eyes.

I never thought about it, but when driving, like when doing everything else in my life, I rotated my head to the left and leaned it left as well, placing my right eye at front and center (every photograph of me shows that's how I "look at the camera"). This placed my dominant eye in the best position to do most of the work, although peripheral vision remained in both eyes. The head turn probably limited peripheral vision on my right, and I can turn my head further to the left than to the right, to this day.

Visual impairment was not my greatest driving hazard in my teens. But my youthful judgment aside, mishaps due to vision were limited to close encounters where distance perception was a factor and were usually at low speed. And like in every activity, I adapted my driving behavior to address the challenges.

As an adult I developed neck and shoulder pain when driving, particularly for long periods. I eventually discovered that I could ease this pain by focusing my mind on left and right peripheral vision simultaneously. Somehow, this caused my head to straighten somewhat and eased the pain. This adaptation foreshadowed lessons I would learn in vision therapy.

15

Concord-Carlisle's Angry Young Man

I recently asked my two younger sisters about how other kids perceived me growing up. They first said that they couldn't remember much since they were much younger (three-and-a-half and seven years), but they did remember me as being popular. Odd. I don't remember it that way at all. A look at my 1964 Concord-Carlisle High School yearbook may explain the discrepancy. My photo is one of very few with no school activities listed; I didn't participate. Below the photo:

ROBERT CROCKETT
"Bobby"
c.c.'s angry young man...has to find out for himself... battles to hide his brilliance... "don't wait up for me, Ma."

I didn't write that. And I remember being hurt by that description of me. But it is what others scribbled throughout my book that is the most telling. They weren't writing about friendships. They were writing about my exploits. I was more notorious than popular. Or maybe I was popular, or could have been popular, but couldn't see.

I had friends. Usually, one at a time. As I look back, I'd guess they were misfits, too. To this day, I prefer one-on-one conversations to groups. I am an introvert, yes. But when you are speaking with only one person, the question never comes up, "Were you speaking to me?"

Maybe it was my substandard vision that prompted my behavior, but I always knew that I would rather experience something than look at it. This often meant creating the experiences, and my friends were often caught up in them. We sometimes got into trouble; other times we didn't get caught.

Misdeeds began early and escalated as I advanced grades in school. Some were pranks, others were acting out in anger and rebellion, and some were even self-harming. For example, the last period one day found me with a friend, skipping class in the copy room of our high school. Together we typed up a memo cancelling school the next day, and one of us signed the principal's name. After we had printed up sufficient copies, we gave them to the girls who usually passed out notices, and they did their thing. Or so we thought. There was no school the next day for my friend and me, nor for a week after. Dad put me to work in our yard with a shovel.

I rebelled against authority at school and with my father at home. Armed with logic and critical thinking, I fought fiercely against illogic and injustice, as I saw it with my eyes. Dad and I argued constantly during my teen years. My father did not really have a childhood himself, yet did his best to love and raise me despite his limitations. His response to my "critical thinking" was discipline. Fortunately, we reconciled long before his death. I appreciate more than ever the obstacles he overcame, and his character and values that I try to live up to.

On my fifteenth birthday, rather than attending a flower show with my father and the family that afternoon, I left my school stuff across the street, took a bus into Boston, a shuttle to New York, and a train to Washington, D.C., where I arrived that night in the pouring rain and found a cheap hotel. The next day I began hitchhiking south. It wasn't until I arrived in Florida that a fellow hitchhiker convinced me to call home. Before I finished high school, I left home again, this time reaching the Chicago stockyards and becoming violently ill sleeping in the cab of a truck. I called home again, and like before, they wired me funds for a bus ticket.

Nobody, including my parents and teachers, understood back then the extent to which vision problems can manifest in these ways. I was variously labelled an underachiever, a behavioral problem, or worse. My grandfather suggested reform school more than once. To say that nobody understood my vision's impact on me would be true, even for me. As I reflect, my hurt feelings from social slights or my own failings probably played a large part in the empathy I've always felt for other people with challenges. Making fun of disabilities or disfigurements disgusts me. And I'm with the underdog from beginning to end!

16

Transcendental Revolutionary

Growing up in Concord, Massachusetts may have stirred the rebel in me. It was and still is an affluent, bedroom community 19 miles from Boston, but it was smaller then and one's ancestors had to have lived there for several generations to be considered "Concordians," which we weren't. Concord's pride was not entirely undeserved, as it claimed many superlatives. It was the oldest inland town in the US, founded in 1635, only 15 years after the Mayflower Pilgrims landed at Plymouth Rock.

Concord's Sleepy Hollow Cemetery hosts the graves of authors Ralph Waldo Emerson, Nathaniel Hawthorne, Henry David Thoreau, the Alcott family, and sculptor Daniel Chester French, known for the Concord Minuteman and the Lincoln Memorial, among many other artists and thinkers. My own parents, after leading notable lives, short and long, rest there now as well.

The fame of these authors isn't what is significant to me; rather it is the message many of them were sharing: transcendentalism. As I understand it, transcendentalism is a belief in inherent human goodness. While I've never followed it formally, I've always felt aligned with it.

The American Revolution began on the nineteenth of April 1775, when Minutemen turned back the British Redcoats at Concord's Old North Bridge.

Emerson memorialized that day in his famous poem, "Concord Hymn":

> By the rude bridge that arched the flood,
> Their flag to April's breeze unfurled,
> Here once the embattled farmers stood,
> And fired the shot heard round the world.

Like the Minutemen, I have always felt comfortable opposing, and even disobeying, rules that I deem unjust. My parents were the first authorities to experience my approach to injustice, but it has sometimes extended to other jurisdictions. In my own defense, I believe that many laws are of significant benefit, and while I joke about being a "scofflaw," I am in most cases law-abiding.

In calling myself a "transcendental revolutionary," I am pointing to the way my mind has worked since childhood. I've always wanted to experience things, be in the action, rather than observe or take pictures. Maybe that life-shaping impulse was because seeing just wasn't good enough.

How much my way of thinking was a product of my way of seeing I hadn't then considered, yet I believe that my questioning of authority and openness to transcendence is an important part of this story, and why this story happened at all.

17

Doctor My Eyes

"Bob, you see things differently from most people. Your vision gives you a different point of view." Those were the words of Dr. Lawrence MacDonald, OD. That was 50 years ago when I was about 20. My mother had come across Dr. MacDonald, and never giving up her hope that my vision would improve, had recommended I see him. I now understand that he was doing pioneering work in the treatment of Binocular Vision Disorders (BVDS). Yet a prominent Boston optometrist who tried unsuccessfully to fit me with contact lenses called Dr. MacDonald a "quack." Misunderstandings about the power of vision therapy are still common among eyecare professionals today.

I understood immediately the double meaning that Dr. MacDonald intended in his statement.

I had long known that I *saw* differently from most people. The new insight was that my condition played a part in interpreting things in a different way than most people. I'd always marched to Thoreau's "different drummer," but I realized that I was shaped not by what I heard, but by how I saw.

I saw Dr. MacDonald a few times. At my first visit, by looking at my posture, he determined that I had been cross-eyed, not wall-eyed as I had thought. He was right, and that impressed me. In his office he had various props, not unlike those a magician might use. Spinning discs seemed to be a theme. He gave me my first "Brock String," a beaded length of twine.

The furniture in his therapy room revealed the fact that his practice focused on young children. Based on my belief that the critical period to achieve fusion had closed, his focus on children, and the fact he never mentioned having adult patients, I didn't hold out much hope. The Brock String was never used and eventually lost.

I was in my fifties before my next-door neighbor in St. Petersburg, Florida, a young optometrist, introduced me to Dr. Sorkin, a doppelganger for Nicolas Cage. His clinic also seemed to be equipped for kids, rather than grown-ups. Again, without a single example of a successfully-treated adult, there seemed little hope of change. I may not have even realized it at the time, but I lacked a role model! I came away with another Brock String, but never used it.

Many people don't know what *strabismus* is, and many strabismics have never been diagnosed; and lack awareness or understanding of their own condition. One thing is for certain though: *stereopsis* (normal binocular vision) and *stereoblindness* are two different ways of *perceiving* and *being* in the world. I believe that the only way to understand both is to experience both and I have.

Now, in my seventies, I better understand how much my way of seeing has shaped me, physically and psychologically. Experts agree. I hope revealing my experiences will help other strabismics to reflect on theirs. By building on individual strengths, many strabismics have excelled in their chosen fields.

Unrelated to strabismus, emergency visits to eye doctors would occur, once in my early fifties, and again a decade later. The first time, it snuck up on me. I hadn't been seeing right for a few minutes before I admitted it to myself. It appeared as if what I was seeing had been torn, like a photograph, then put back together without matching the edges, and without all the pieces. And, particularly when I closed my eyes, I saw jagged, kaleidoscopic patterns of colored light, arcing across my view.

When I called Dr. Sorkin, he told me to come in immediately. These symptoms might indicate a torn retina, something which, he told me, had to be addressed within 24 hours. His examination showed that my retina was intact, but that I had suffered what he called an "ocular migraine" also called an "aura." I am grateful that I didn't have the intense pain that often follows the aura for many people afflicted with migraine headaches. Instead, I had a mild feeling of malaise that continued past the 20 to 30-minutes of the visual display. I have had ocular migraines over the years since, occurring at random intervals. Triggers may include stress and chocolate, neither of which I am able to avoid altogether.

The second vision event that sent me to the doctor occurred in my early sixties. Most people are familiar with, and give little thought to, the things we call "floaters." They are the little specks that we can sometimes see when we are looking at a blank wall or the sky. Floaters seem to float up or down, all together in a stream, but will suddenly jump when we "look" at them. They are normal. What I began to see in my right eye, and what grew rapidly throughout the day, was a grotesque monster-like image along the edge of my vision, seemingly made of floater material. It was like a great segmented worm, standing there on the right, reaching its single claw across the top. As night approached, I also noticed flashes of white light that appeared along the edges of my vision whenever I moved my eyes quickly.

I was travelling at the time, and again, fearing retinal detachment of the one eye I depended upon, I found an ophthalmologist to see me after hours. There was detachment all right, but thankfully it wasn't my retina. The vitreous humor, the clear, gelatinous substance that fills the eyeball and keeps it from collapsing, had permanently detached itself from my retina, causing those effects. In addition to the monster, the visual impairment grew to appear as if multiple dark veils were draped over my eye. As the doctor predicted, the effect would eventually subside and what remained would be easier to ignore. Unlike the ocular migraines, which have continued, posterior vitreous detachment could only occur once more, in the other eye, which it did a few years later. That time I didn't call a doctor.

18

Spinning Out of Academia

Unenthusiastically, but without other prospects, I had applied to a few universities and been accepted by the University of Massachusetts at Amherst, its sole campus at the time. I was a classic "underachiever" with lots of IQ and aptitude, but erratic grades. Test scores were high, but where homework had been required, I had done poorly. So, off to college I went, majoring in physics, but with no idea what to expect or how to cope.

I'd spent most of the preceding summer traveling in Europe with my parents and three sisters, much of that time in close quarters. I was as ready as any college freshman to unshackle myself.

"Freedom" had been my rallying cry since my childhood and suddenly I was free! Did I ever screw that up!

I really wasn't able to read effectively, never mind study, and I didn't understand the system at all. I pledged a fraternity. I fell in love and had my heart broken. My first semester ended with academic probation and my second began with disciplinary suspension. They reinstated me the next year and I went back to register. After the first day, I left.

I thought then it was the long lines, or that most of the students were there to have fun at their parents' expense, and I knew there were more enjoyable places to be. I realize now that my vision's impact on my reading ability was actually behind my abrupt decision to leave college. I'd barely opened my textbooks the first time and had gained no new skills to address the problem. When I could get myself to focus on reading it took so many false starts and such a long time to read a page that I was discouraged from making any effort. Yet there are rare times that reading something interesting can pull me along for hours in the push-pull phenomenon I described earlier. I don't understand this, but I don't think it's laziness. Is suppression simply easier when one is engaged in, or distracted by the story? I don't know, but the decision I made that day to leave college set my life on a new course, one where I could adapt more readily to my vision challenges.

19

Aviation

I never had trouble finding jobs, and I tried a few after the University of Massachusetts. I started at the local Howard Johnson's washing dishes, and was promptly promoted to night maintenance. At midnight I'd show up as everyone was leaving, and I was locked in with a mop until eight the next morning. It suited me fine. It also gave me time to take on other jobs in the daytime. I found a small apartment in Bedford and eventually took a job nearby as a milkman. I was single, had an income, and was off work before noon.

Earlier, I wrote that my mother had explained how my vision was the reason I had trouble hitting or catching a baseball. She'd also been telling me since my earliest memory that I'd never be able to be a pilot. Most boys in our culture would talk about playing baseball, but why was she telling me I couldn't be a pilot when I was so young? I never questioned it until recently. But now I think I've found the answer.

The little house on Old Bedford Road on the Concord/Bedford line, where I lived until I was five, was just off the end of a runway at Hanscom Field. Airplanes were landing or departing, low and directly overhead! What boy growing up under a flight path wouldn't want to be a pilot?

Mom must have seen that interest and set out early to protect me from greater disappointment later on. My interest didn't disappear, though. Later, I watched low-flying F-86 Sabre Jets and every small plane that caught my ear.

And I assembled and flew balsa wood model planes, some launched by hand and others propelled by long rubber bands that I painstakingly wound. My favorite glider was the one that got away. Its wings folded back along its side and it could be launched like a slingshot with a long elastic, straight up into the air. At the top, its wings sprang open, and it began its glide, way above any glider I'd flown before. The very first time I flew it, rising thermals must have caught it, for we chased it up the side of Nashawtuc Hill before losing sight of it forever.

Hanscom Field, a combined municipal and Air Force airport, was near my apartment, and at the age of 20, I took my first flying lesson. Pat McHugh, my flight instructor, had started his career as a crop duster in the Mississippi Delta, the birthplace of the airline with the same name. He loved to fly and it showed. We did things with that little Cessna 150 that it may not have been certified for, and he might have shown me what was illegal by example once or twice. He taught me the memory tools or mnemonics that pilots use as mental check lists. Further, he taught me good habits; he always seemed to have a rolled-up chart ready to swat my hand if it wandered from the throttle on approach. Eventually, the garbled voices on the radio became intelligible. And Pat taught me how to scan my instruments, how to look above and below me for aircraft changing altitude, and around the horizon for the greatest threat, other planes at my own altitude! I learned to look to the side and down when landing to best judge my height above, and alignment with, the runway. I never mentioned my vision issues to Pat. Since I had told no one else, why start now?

The license required passing a written test, a flight test and a medical exam. I did well on my written and managed to pass my flight test. The medical exam was rudimentary, carried out by a local pilot/doctor. There was an eye chart for acuity, but nothing to assess binocularity. That was 1966 in a rural doctor's office and I was not applying to fly airliners. Still, I'm surprised that I wasn't given a simple binocularity test, even then.

When I think about distance perception based on the angle of convergence of fused eyes, I don't know that it has much effect on judging the most important distance for a pilot: height from the ground when landing. I already had ways of judging how high I was. Motion parallax was probably most valuable.

The angle of the edge of the runway through my side window told me how close the ground was. I had a more likely risk once I was there. The wings of a typical small plane like I was flying stuck out about 15 feet on each side. I had very little confidence at that distance and was more afraid of clipping another plane's wingtip while taxiing than I was of dropping onto the runway or crashing into it.

What I also lacked was something I had never experienced: any sense of a panoramic view. My greatest threat probably wasn't landing but was failing to spot another airplane in the sky with me. First there's the battle for the middle that I've spoken of, where my brain is hiding from me the second image of everything. Can I ever trust that it won't hide the first image too? Can I trust what I see? And then there's the blind spot, which each eye has. It is where the optic nerve connects to the back of the eyeball. With stereoscopic vision, each eye covers for the other eye's blind spot. With suppression, a blind spot can remain, regardless of which eye I use. And to make things harder, the horizon is the most difficult part of the sky in which to spot another plane, and an airplane can present as a slim profile, particularly if headed right for you. Sometimes a plane can appear out of the sun in an instant. I knew this was my weakness, and I was doubly vigilant.

My mom and I never spoke of her prediction and she never flew with me. My dad flew with me once, after commenting on the 90 per cent grade I received on my written test that I "would only crash 10 percent of the time."

A student pilot's first big milestone is the supervised solo. Mine came as a surprise. In the 12 hours of flying that we'd done so far, we had taken short flights to nearby airports, but wherever we went, we concentrated on take-offs and especially landings. Every flight, after all, ends in contact with the earth and must be done effectively each time. Pilots joke about any landing you walk away from being a good one, but all good aviators practice them often. We were doing touch-and-go's in the pattern at Hanscom when Pat told me to stop the plane and let him out beside the runway. I was shocked, but he closed the door and stepped away. I realized I was about to make my first solo flight. After calling the tower, I shut off the carburetor heat, pushed in the throttle and when flying speed was reached, I eased back the yoke and was airborne. I did a few circuits that day and I was too busy to pay attention to my vision, but I was aware of the freedom that I felt and the fact that I was flying on my own regardless of my mom's prediction. As for my vision, I treated flying the same as everything else: I adapted as best I could, and I kept my issues to myself.

It took me a year to earn my private pilot license. It seemed like forever, as I studied and saved money for lessons. But it was worth it and, as I looked around, I didn't know anyone else my age who could fly.

Flying, especially in rented aircraft, has always been relatively expensive. I was able to get others to pay for the flight time required to pilot complex and multi-engine aircraft. In the summer of 1973, I logged about 100 hours in fabric-covered taildraggers, spotting swordfish for commercial harpooning in the North Atlantic! When I wasn't spending up to 12 hours a day over the ocean, the plane was mine to use. I loved to fly; I was free. My world, if not my vision, finally had three dimensions. Although I never set out to defy my mother, I had achieved what I had always been told I couldn't.

20

An Arc of Boatbuilding

Thoughts of boats and airplanes must reside together in my brain, as both have attracted me almost interchangeably. Between my flying experiences, I went to work for my dad, and that, circuitously, led to a career in boatbuilding.

In addition to *Flowery Talks*, Dad had written books about flowers and gardening, published by Doubleday. Time-Life Books then asked him to adapt the encyclopedia he was developing into their Encyclopedia of Gardening, and he asked me and my new wife if we'd like to take over his sales territories for him for a couple of years. I had some experience in selling, including a brief prior period when I made a solo midwestern sales trip for *Flowery Talks*. Despite my introversion, I was comfortable one-on-one with people. I was proud of my Dad and knew the effectiveness of my product. Dad's expertise and passion for sharing his love would lead to hosting the popular PBS television show, *Crockett's Victory Garden* until his death in 1979.

Rather than rely on motel beds and restaurant meals, we opted to travel in a series of RVs, with a large dog. Our territories were the West, where I had traveled with my Dad, plus New England. The importance of certain holidays to florists meant that there were times they just didn't want to see a salesman, so I stayed away. That led to

two winters in a row in Mexico, and two summer trips to
Nova Scotia, my paternal grandmother's childhood home.

While we traveled, I made lists of what I might want to
do next, when this work was over. While in San Francisco,
on a whim, I interviewed at the Canadian consulate to
immigrate to Nova Scotia. The interviewer noticed that
I had sold life insurance in the past and asked if I'd be
willing to do that again. I began to say no, when she said
that if I was willing, I'd have enough points...

We were accepted, and in September 1973, and with my
list of potential careers, we moved to Nova Scotia. I had
some uninteresting job interviews in Halifax for a couple
of days, then returned to Lunenburg for the weekend. We
met a young American immigrant our age, working at the
library. Her husband had found work as a boatbuilder and
she thought I could do the same. She told me that if I asked
Ted Snyder for a job at his shipyard, he would say to come
back in two weeks, and if I did, he would hire me. Sure
enough, he said to come back in two weeks. But I went to
another shipyard and they asked if I could start the next
day. I took that job. Boatbuilding, after all, had been on my
list all along, even though I had no direct experience.

I knew the moment I walked into the big Quonset hut
and saw the hull of the *Sheila Yeats*, that I had to work on
her. It didn't require two eyes to tell that this boat looming
above me existed in at least three dimensions. She was
not just big and beamy, but she was beautiful as well. The
hull was built of rare Port Orford cedar, and the caulking
seams between the planks had been filled with strips of the
same wood, planed and sanded smooth. A light, yellowish
creamy color with an indiscernible grain, it appeared to be

velvet soft. It was topped by a wide, thicker sheer strake along the deck edge made of mahogany. Fifty feet long on deck and sixteen feet wide, the *Sheila Yeats* was a replica of a Civil War era sailing vessel being built for Geoff Pope of Minnesota. The launching would not take place until long after I left the yard, for financial reasons, but Geoff became linked to my family until his death.

Geoff was a modest man with big dreams and the courage to pursue them. Approaching retirement age when he began the project, it wasn't his first. Unlike a lot of adventurers, he didn't waste time telling tales of past feats; instead, he always focused on the next. For example, he seldom spoke of his voyage on a friend's yacht sailing around Cape Horn, considered among the most arduous of passages. And it was after he passed away that I learned of his 1930s voyage by canoe, with one other fellow, from Manhattan Island, New York to Nome, Alaska. Following the old explorers' route, it was recorded as the longest canoe trip of the time in the Guinness Book of World Records.

I worked in the Quonset hut for two years, learning from men who had been building wooden boats their entire lives, who had learned the trade from their fathers and uncles. Lunenburg, Nova Scotia was famous for its wooden shipbuilding. The schooner *Bluenose*, stamped on the Canadian dime, was built here, along with her replica *Bluenose II*, and the *Bounty* in the Marlon Brando film *Mutiny on the Bounty*. My workmates had built these vessels and others. I liked hearing their endless stories and learning the skills of the trade. Meanwhile, at home, I was slowly building an 18-foot sailing skiff and starting a family.

I opened the Rose Bay Boat Shop in 1975, expanding from the one-car garage where I had built my skiff into a multi-building complex next to my home on Lower Rose Bay. In 1980, with venture capital backing, a partner and I began a new company, building custom commercial boats nearby, based on a business plan that I had written. I didn't keep count of the boats I built in that decade, and I seldom built more than a few at the same time. They included fishing and sailing boats, walrus-hunting boats for the Arctic, fast rescue boats for the offshore oil industry, and a couple of twelve-meter yachts. We were technological leaders and we built gorgeous boats. I employed some fine people and did my best to provide for them, as well as serve our customers.

I learned that my employees used to refer to me amongst themselves as the "Inspector." There is no question that I had a critical eye, essential to building boats, in my opinion. Stereoblindness may have benefitted me in two ways, one simple, the other more subtle.

Much of the work of boatbuilding is close and detailed: taking measurements, scribing shapes, and cutting them on a bandsaw. It wasn't necessary for me to squint one eye to sight a cut line or to make a precise mark on a workpiece from a ruler. I had only one line of sight, my dominant eye, and there was no confusion. Fit and finish are not unique to boatbuilding, of course, but stereoblindness wasn't a big detriment and may have made some tasks easier.

Boats are all curves. Cabin sides curve and lean in at the same time. Decks and cabin tops are cambered and even below decks, every corner is rounded to avoid injuring crew at sea. Hulls are the shapeliest of all, and in most cases consist of compound curves. Compound curves are difficult to make but provide the greatest options for efficient operation in a boat's fluid environment, consisting of water and air. We see compound curves most commonly on automobiles, where over a century they have gradually become more streamlined to where they all look alike today. Water is a lot denser than air, so I guess that's why shapeliness has been crucial for boat hulls since the first dugout canoe.

A curve is fair or not fair. We think of fair as pleasing to the eye, and that is so with boats. More specifically, fairness describes a line or a surface that is smooth, without flaws, and that flows evenly from the curvature at one place to that at another. Fairness must be in the design of the boat, but that doesn't guarantee it in the execution. Various techniques are used to ensure fairness of a compound curve, but the best way to inspect it is with the play of light on the surface. And, for that, I think a single eye may be better than two. That's because of how light reflects on a shiny, curved surface. A distant light source reflecting on a nearby hull now appears in two slightly different places on the surface. I think the double reflection obscures flaws that I could better detect with my single-eyed vision, earning me the nickname "Inspector."

In 1983, no longer building boats with my own hands, but responsible for feeding a 35-person workforce with boatbuilding contracts, I sold my interest to my partners and moved on.

I had pursued freedom all my life and that included freedom from routine. My boatbuilding had always been custom or very specialized. Boats are inherently complex, and I built many types and sizes of boats in wood, welded aluminum, and fiberglass. Being in business for myself and doing something different every day suited me just fine. Aside from the time selling *Flowery Talks,* where I was paid a pure commission and was out of touch for days or weeks, I rarely kept a full-time job for someone else for more than 13 months. Oddly, that unlucky number seemed to have doomed my employment several times over the years.

To my great delight and benefit, at least from my perspective, my aversion to jobs has afforded me a wonderful variety of experiences, both in working and avoiding work. In my youth, I had hitchhiked across Canada or the United States six times, and deep into Mexico, often without a dime in my pocket. After that, I was never again afraid of being broke. I also realized that I could choose joy as a way to live my life, and I did.

Selling had also been a theme: I had sold Stanley Home Products door-to-door in my early teens, insurance in my twenties, and several other things before moving to Nova Scotia.

Then, after ten years building boats, I delved into business and finance, consulting for other entrepreneurs and making small investments in a few businesses. One of those, a medical diagnostics company in Halifax, Nova Scotia, has done well in the decades since.

The summer of 1996 brought the *Picton Castle* to Lunenburg, and I agreed to manage its conversion from a rusty diesel freighter into a 179-foot three-masted barque, a square-rigged tall ship. My son, Rigel, had sailed with

the owner on a large schooner the summers he was nine
and ten; and when he finished college he joined the crew
preparing the ship. At the end of 1997, he sailed from
Lunenburg on a voyage around the world. (He later wrote a
book about the voyage entitled *Fair Wind and Plenty of It*).

With Rigel halfway around the world and his sister,
Laurel, in university, I moved to Florida in 1998. This time
I was managing the construction of a 123-foot mega-yacht
in a yard full of them, and when the 13 months were up, I
left. I was going back to school, and this time I was going
to succeed!

The University of South Florida's Board of Regents had
just informed the Dean of the School of Business that, if a
suitably qualified candidate applied to their Executive MBA
program who lacked an undergraduate degree, they could
make an exception. Along I came, with a very high GMAT
score and an interesting work history, so they accepted
me. A Fortune Magazine article on executive coaching
caught my eye about that time, and I enrolled in a two-year
remote training program at the same time as my MBA. It
was entirely over the telephone, so my ability to visualize
came into play more than my vision.

I was 52 years old, and few things in my work or
personal life since youth had been particularly affected by
my vision. The reading and writing that had been required
had always been brief enough not to pose a problem, and I
had adapted otherwise. But now I had been accepted into a
rigorous program that would require a lot of reading. How
would I manage it?

For one thing, I found that maturity made a difference.
I knew what I wanted and that it would take effort and

resourcefulness to accomplish it. Sometimes, rarely, I would get caught up in the reading and be pulled along, but mostly it was pure, painful push, word by word, trying to capture the meaning all the while. The most helpful aid I found was to write the precise time that I began each page at the top, checking as I finished on how long it had taken. Paying attention to my pace in that way seemed to help keep it steadier.

I finished the program at the top of my class, which felt like a personal triumph after all the vision problems I had experienced at school. Meanwhile, my daughter met and married my study group partner, and my son safely completed his circumnavigation and married his college sweetheart. They each gave me a grandchild.

Earning an MBA broadened and deepened my understanding of business, but the coach training changed my life, as is often the case for those who seek coaches. Question: "How many coaches does it take to change a lightbulb?" Answer: "The lightbulb has to want to change."

Coaching is powerful for three reasons. As a coach, I knew the clients had their own answers, I just had to find the questions. I became their first and only partner who didn't have a personal agenda for them, and I had a kit of life skills that I could suggest with permission. A family physician client, who had said, "I'm next" after teasing her husband about having a coach, asked me after a few weeks as a client, "This is about self-awareness isn't it?"

Like others who had found their way into life coaching in its early days, I had always wanted to improve myself, especially if it was relatively fast and easy. And we all wanted to help others, yet offering unsolicited advice didn't work. I was able to help people make the changes they wanted. I loved coaching, and became its beneficiary, quitting a lifetime of smoking, developing several good habits, and ultimately "pre-tiring" in my fifties.

And so, I entered my sixties.

21

I Now See How I Saw

As mentioned earlier, I understood that I had "monocular vision" and that I was an "alternator." Mom said I was lucky that I had become an alternator, or I could have lost much of the vision in my non-dominant eye (amblyopia). It is important to understand that while I was seeing what was in front of me with one eye at a time, I had peripheral vision with both eyes, all the time. Essentially, my mind was filtering out duplicates! Because my eyes didn't align perfectly, the images didn't meet in the same place on my two retinas, and my brain created double images. Whenever my eyes were open, my brain was hiding one or the other set of duplicate images from me! There was always a place, on one side or the other, where the dominant eye view didn't line up with its partners, but it's blurry on the edges anyway...

How did I alternate? Sometimes it was involuntary, as when one eye had a distinctly better vantage point. But I could choose the eye I was seeing through at will. I cannot count the hours I spent in a classroom, entertaining myself by moving an object outdoors from one windowpane to another, without moving my head. I didn't know the mechanism and I still am not sure. Did I move my eyes slightly to bring the thing I was observing into view of the other eye? Or did my mind somehow get my brain to throw some hidden switch?

Alternator or not, my right eye was definitely in charge. It had practically 20/20 acuity. It also appeared larger on my face. As a part of the suppression, my brain had also closed my left eye a bit, compensating by permanently raising my left eyebrow. It wasn't just my face that was crooked. I didn't understand the extent at the time, but suppression would affect my entire left side for a lifetime.

Whether it was because of the surgery or merely innate binocularity, my eyes were locked in near parallel tracks. When one eye (usually my dominant right eye) moved to look at something, my left eye moved the same amount, regardless of the object's distance. If I looked at myself in a mirror, for example, my right eye would turn in to see the center of my reflection and my left eye would move out to the left, along with it, reinforcing the impression I had for many years that I was wall-eyed (exotropic) rather than cross-eyed (esotropic).

Once I understood this trait in my early thirties, I began the practice, when looking at one person, to look at their right eye with my left, and vice versa. I hoped this would prevent my left eye from appearing to look away. I was still uncertain whether my left eye turned in or out.

It's also worth noting that what I call a "floating third eye" has been a recurring image since I can remember. This is not an eye in the center of my forehead or anyone else's. When looking directly at a person, I would see a second image of their right eye below, and to my left, of the real one. I don't know how much my brain adjusted my eye muscles after my second surgery, but my left eye rotated slightly, as well as turned up and in, relative to my right eye. Seeing a duplicate image of the other person's eye outside of their real one and obviously produced by my non-dominant left eye, led me to believe that my eye was turned out and not in. I was mistaken. The fact that the lens of the eye projects the image upside down on the retina, caused my eye, which turned up and in, to see the double image of the other person's eye, down and out. Whew!

Usually, no other part of the person's face appears, just an identical eye floating on their cheekbone. As my vision therapy progressed, I would gradually see more of people's faces and eventually two heads and two bodies, but it always seemed to start with the third eye.

This third eye image has been so persistent that it used to appear on talking heads on the television. I wonder, why the eye? Why has it been so prevalent and persistent? Is it because the eyes are windows to the soul? Or is it because, in my efforts to look people in the eye when I'm face-to-face, I somehow weaken the suppression? I don't know, and I've wondered if other strabismics experience the same thing.

I told nobody that they had a third eye floating on their cheek, nor did I describe my 2D world. It would have been difficult, maybe impossible, to relate it to someone with normal vision. You cannot simply cover an eye and see as a stereoblind person does.

I didn't learn the terms "stereoblindness" or "binocular vision disorder" until recently, but I find them more descriptive than "strabismus." While "cross-eyed" or "wall-eyed" describe physical appearance, they also do little to shine light on the underlying condition.

What a stereoblind person sees is not flat, as if on a single plane. And it isn't like it's painted on the inside of a big sphere, yet that may be closer. I knew that some things were nearer than others, and my eyes gave me most of those clues. But, because I was seeing from only one eye and one vantage point at a time, my brain couldn't use geometry to gauge distance. I wrote about the difficulty seeing moving objects like baseballs. To that I would add doorknobs, which I often missed when I reached for them. Fortunately, though, geometry only aids distance perception up to a few feet away, so I could adapt for most activities.

Eyesight, vision and perception are three different things, in my opinion. Visual acuity, each eye's ability to read letters on a chart, is too often all anyone knows about how they or their children see.

Vision takes place in the brain, which has the responsibility and honor to make sense of this extraordinary stream of information from sensors in two different locations on our faces. One out of 25 brains is being fed information that is distinctly different from each eye. Brains can respond in different ways. Usually, the eyes will use a combination of means, including turning one eye toward the nose, decreasing acuity in that eye, and somehow, magically suppressing duplicate images it receives. Tragically, some strabismics suffer ongoing double vision (diplopia).

I understood about my eyesight and vision growing up, and it was a part of my consciousness and my life. I lived secretly with its limitations and rarity. Dr. MacDonald's comment about *how* I saw things (perception) suddenly brought my life into focus, as it were. I *was* different because I *saw* things differently.

A one-eyed view of the world, perceptively, is different than a stereoscopic one. In giving up what it has never known, three-dimensional vision, my brain chose a very rational view. People with normal vision see double images all the time. If you look at a pencil in front of you, the background will be double. Not for me. I saw only one of everything, regardless. My brain only showed me things as it knew them to be – singular. My love of the precise, of mathematics, physics, and difficult puzzles with clear answers may have been linked to my singular perception.

Another thread besides my love of precision was my distrust of authority and the status quo. Did it stem in part from the fact that I couldn't trust my own eyes? I learned very early that I had to read things, particularly strings of numbers, very carefully. And I certainly didn't trust my vision around any precipitous edge. Bordering on acrophobia, I carefully avoided cliffs, rooftops, and even low railings, although I had no problem climbing a 100-foot mast at sea.

And a third thread is a constant quest to learn hidden knowledge. Perhaps it ties the other two together, somehow. Is perception connected to vision? I don't know, but it also may have stemmed from vision I didn't trust.

I had accepted my limitations early, including that I'd never fly fighters or airliners, but I learned to fly anyway. Although I knew that my eyes worked differently, my disorder made me aware of that fact in the way I used them every day. I accepted my condition as simple reality – neither good nor bad. By this, I mean that I never felt like I was a victim. Although my life sucked at times, it was simply my fate, along with the continuing task of learning to cope.

22

The Secret Society
of Strabismics

When did you last talk to a cross-eyed person about
their condition? Unless you're a professional or a family
member, I'll bet never. I didn't, even as a strabismic myself.
Yet one in 25 people shares the condition – in fact, it's so
secret we don't even acknowledge each other.

Until I was 70 years old, I never told a soul outside my
immediate family, not even my best friends, about my
condition. As a youth, I let my friends and teachers draw
their own conclusions about why I couldn't, or wouldn't,
play ball.

There may be other reasons we don't talk about
strabismus. Many strabismics don't know that their vision
is abnormal. They have only been tested for visual acuity,
not binocularity, apparently.

And what language would we use? I was afflicted, so
words like "cross-eyed" and "wall-eyed" seemed coarse and
hurtful. Yet they are the most common and descriptive
of the condition. In Britain, it's "squint." "Cock-eyed
Optimist," a song from Rodgers and Hammerstein's *South
Pacific* inspired this book's name. "Strabismus" is the
technical word for all misaligned eyes, but few people
know its meaning.

Embarrassment and shame also need mentioning.
I have felt both at times about my appearance and my

challenges. It's important to acknowledge that "cosmetic surgery" had improved my outward appearance, and I didn't bear the burden of others with more visible conditions. Often feeling "broken" myself, I have never wanted to embarrass others similarly afflicted by speaking of it. Speaking to them today, the most important thing I would say is that straight eyes and 3D vision can be achieved without surgery.

23

"Stereo Sue"

I tore the article from a *New Yorker* magazine after it came out in 2006, read it and tucked it away. Oliver Sacks had written "Stereo Sue" about a professor of neurobiology with a condition like mine who had become stereoscopic at the age of 48.[7] I didn't know then of Oliver Sacks's own extraordinary story, described in his book, *The Man Who Mistook His Wife for a Hat.*

Sue had strabismus and had undergone three surgeries. She clearly had found studying easier than I had, as her career choice indicates. A role model had finally appeared, an adult who had overcome my condition! Yet, I didn't act, except to save the article.

In 2009, Dr. Susan Barry published her own version of her story in *Fixing My Gaze: A Scientist's Journey into Seeing in Three Dimensions.* I came across the book in March 2014 and I was hooked!

Before reading the book, I had previously only one memory of my time in the hospital, playing with the telephone truck in my high-sided bed. However, when Sue shared memories of having her bandages changed, suddenly I remembered the nurse changing mine. I broke into tears and sobbed – I must have been crying for the

---

7   Oliver Sacks, "Stereo Sue." *The New Yorker*, June 19, 2006: 64

little boy that I had been. I'll write more about this later, but I agree with those who say we store trauma in our bodies, and Sue's story had touched my eyes.

This was my story as much as it was hers, and although she had become stereoscopic almost by accident while she was receiving vision therapy for a seemingly unrelated problem, it seemed to me that I might do it through intention! In fact, in the book, she revealed that people who had read "Stereo Sue" contacted her and shared similar transformations. I knew it could be done, but I also knew there were some things I wasn't able to do alone, and this was one of them.

Fifty years had passed since I had given much thought to addressing the everyday challenges of strabismus. Now, with a credible role model, for the first time I felt the hope of seeing like others.

I needed help, and Dr. Barry provided a resource section in *Fixing My Gaze*. I was looking for an optometrist trained specifically in vision therapy. Trouble was, there were none in the entire province of Nova Scotia and the maritime provinces. This called for a different approach, and I was ready to do whatever it took to make it happen.

24

Two Years on Hold

So, I set out to find a local optometrist who might like
to learn vision therapy, in order to help me. I studied the
online biographies of every local optometrist, along with
patients' comments and anything else I could find. Among
all of them one person stood out. Doctor Angela Dobson
hadn't begun her professional career as an optometrist, but
as a geologist. And she had moved from Western Canada
to the Maritimes, a big shift in geography and culture. She
appeared to be someone open to change.

I contacted Dr. Dobson and asked if she'd be willing
to read Dr. Barry's book before my first appointment. She
agreed. It may have been in a subsequent conversation,
but I also admit to applying a bit of pressure by telling her
that I had cancer and wanted to see in 3D before I die.

For six months, each time I called her, I got the same
answer – she was learning more and would get back to me
when she was ready.

When we finally met in her office, I found her
delightfully energetic. She looked directly at me and
smiled constantly. She assessed my vision with the usual
instruments, prescribed new glasses, and took the time
to go through a pile of photocopies with me. Each page
was an exercise for me to do at home. Many were physical
exercises, others involved only my eyes. Some involved

pencils and pick-up sticks; and of course, there was the Brock String and its beads. She ran through them all with me.

Then she dropped a bomb! She was traveling around the world with her family and would be away for a year. She would be in touch when she returned. I was to keep up the exercises. By the time I returned to pick up my new lenses, she was gone.

As for the exercises, they sat on my desk for a little while before I stepped up one day and began the first one. I didn't last a minute. I'm no fool. Without help, I knew I wasn't capable of doing enough exercises to make any difference at all. And I wasn't prepared to search for another optometrist. After all, Dr. Dobson had gotten back to me as promised – so I waited, and I eventually filed the exercises away and forgot all about them.

Then, two years after my first contact with Dr. Dobson, my phone rang. The caller told me that Dr. Dobson had opened a new practice and wanted me to come in for an assessment. She also told me that the Doctor had arranged a special discount for me, as I had inspired her career change.

And what changes she had made! Since I had last seen her, she had sold her share in her previous practice, traveled around the globe with her family for three months, and spent the rest of the time studying and planning her practice. In fact, she was already underway, using vision therapy to help a growing clientele of traumatic brain injury patients. They adored her, and she was bringing them results that they hadn't gotten elsewhere. I would be her only adult patient with strabismus since infancy.

25

Vision Sense

Only now as I reflect on it, do I understand how fittingly Doctor Dobson named her new practice, Vision Sense.

With inspiring energy and optimism, Angela greeted me every time with a big smile. We met in a large room that looked like a day care center after the kids had gone home. In fact, it was equipped for children and adults, and many of the amusements were directly related to vision. There were a couple of rotating discs, large and small. On the large one, I could practice placing pegs in holes as it rotated, all while wearing weird lenses that would displace the images I saw. A little like arcade games of my childhood.

Other things involved balance more than vision; in fact, some were done with my eyes closed, or with one eye covered, or with more weird lenses. One entire wall was covered in cabinet doors from floor to ceiling, all unmarked. From these, Angela (I had pulled my age rank on her by this time and was calling her by her first name) would present many surprise exercises, like she was Captain Kangaroo or some such entertainer of children.

That's not how each hour-long session began, however. First, we would sit facing each other and talk. Sometimes she would have me sit on a bench, other times I would sit in a chair. She would take notes as I related my experiences for the week, and I asked and answered questions. She often had an assistant, sometimes a young traumatic brain injury patient, also taking notes to supplement her own. We would spend whatever time was necessary for this. She agreed that I would be most successful if I understood all I could about what I was doing and why.

I went to Angela's office every week for a year, then every few weeks for many more months.

The Vision Sense office also included a reception area with the requisite displays of eyeglass frames. In her small examination office, she would sit on a stool next to me during periodic assessments, manipulating lenses and asking me repeatedly, "Which is clearer, one or two?" as she took copious notes, and we discussed my condition and progress.

There is a windowless room behind reception where, in utter darkness, Angela would show me points of light: red, green, white, yellow. Points of light in the dark are too distinct to allow suppression. Using penlights while I wore varying lenses, she would move these lights relative to each other and ask me what I saw. This was an emotionally challenging exercise. Never was it clearer to me that my eyes weren't working together than when, as one light slowly approached and neared another in the darkness, it would suddenly jump to the other side, unaccounted for by the slight movement of the penlights in her hand. Of course, it wasn't the light that had jumped, but my eye. This was a familiar exercise and was always stressful because it was clear how little control I had over my eyes.

In the same dark room, I sat alone for long periods of time staring into the large end of a long, black funnel shaped to fit my face. At the small end 18 inches away was a light source, and various filters were inserted to change the colors, which were shades of red and green. This was my first introduction to syntonics, or optometric phototherapy. Angela would later give me colored glasses to wear at home.

There was a trampoline in the hall behind the dark room with charts containing various images, where I spent time bouncing and calling out colors while doing weird exercises. Sometimes, Angela lowered a ball on a string from the ceiling to eye level. Called a Marsden Ball, it is about three inches in diameter, white, and covered with black letters and numbers. Each time I pushed the ball away, I called out the letter or number I had touched. For another exercise, I stood facing a wall and drew large circles on it with first one hand then another, using different eyes. I honestly couldn't see how most of these exercises could help, yet they clearly have. And she kept it from being boring, because there was always another exercise to try.

In another small room she had a machine that could actually track the individual motion of each of my eyes as I attempted to read, and other strange Dickensian devices.

Patience is something I believe I've learned a lot about in my lifetime, but I will admit that there were times with Angela that I would just stop doing an exercise and refuse to go on. Petulant might even be the word. I was frustrated with what I saw as little progress and with my inability to make my eyes work properly.

We spoke of "popping." Susan Barry in her book, had said that her vision "popped" when she first saw in 3D.

Angela made some predictions about when my eyes would pop. Those times came and went without a pop, and she stopped predicting. But Angela never doubted that I would succeed, and her optimism kept me going. I began calling her "Pollyangela," my twist on Pollyanna.

26

The Road to 3D

Vision therapy, although obscure to many, including a large percentage of optometrists and ophthalmologists, is a well-developed science. It offers many tools, practices and modalities, and there is much integration, but there are essential steps in treating strabismus.

The first is to "bring up" the vision in the non-dominant (my left) eye. While it involved brief patching of my right eye for some exercises, that was not the primary practice.

A popular tool, the Brock String, is anchored at one end a couple of yards away, with the near end held to the tip of the nose, pulling the string tight. Two or three beads can be slid to different positions along the string, held there by friction. The object is to focus on one bead at a time, and to see it with both eyes. A person with normal stereopsis would see two string images crossing through that bead, and the other beads would be doubled along that "X." That was not what I saw!

Frustratingly, I could only see the strings with one eye at a time: therefore, only one string image. And what I saw wasn't encouraging. While the string I saw with my left eye was almost horizontal, the same string, seen by my right, extended obliquely from lower left to upper right! And I just couldn't get them to enter a particular bead in the same place. Mostly, the images would fade in and out, sometimes leaving the left eye image, sometimes the right. It was difficult to do for more than a minute or two at a time, even though I understood the promised benefits.

The second step in vision therapy is to facilitate the eyes working together. A prism was included in my left lens prescription, with its base, (thickest part) angled down and out. That meant I wouldn't have to employ my eye muscles very much to align my eyes, should they wish to cooperate. As for the rotation of my eye, I would have to rely on muscles and my brain, as there is no prism that can correct for that.

I'd worn a prism in my left lens for at least 20 years, prescribed by an earlier optometrist. It only compensated for the horizontal deviation of my left eye and not the vertical, as the new prism did. The original doctor told me explicitly that the turn would get worse over time, as the eye becomes accustomed to the prism. A couple of interesting conclusions might be drawn. One is that I must have gotten even better at suppression, allowing for the fact that the turn was optically negated. The other is the fact that the doctor expected my eyes to cross more over time implying a further effort at suppression.

Incidentally, the prism works both ways. Light bends to make a person I'm looking at appear at the same place in both eyes. Light going the other way makes my crossed eyes look straight to the viewer.

27

Homework, Again

I was 70 when I started seeing Angela at Vision Sense. I had adapted somehow to the homework requirements of an MBA, yet I had no habits that would help me improve my vision during all those hours each week at home. Some exercises were the same ones that had sat for a long time on my desk while she went back to school; others were new, but I was still slow to start any homework. I'd had a similar problem with music lessons both as a child and adult – the week would go by and I'd practice for a few minutes before my lesson. But the teachers knew, and soon I didn't even try to fool them.

Dr. Dobson was different. She didn't make me feel guilty, but instead offered me options from which to choose and praised whatever I'd done. Besides the pile of exercises, which I never picked up, there was the ubiquitous Brock String. I had one strung near my desk and occasionally I would pick it up and try for a minute to get two strings to cross at a bead. Even though I never kept at it more than a minute, slowly I began to see part of the "X" I sought, in the form of a "Y." They still skewed terribly, but change began, if not improvement.

After a while, I added another exercise for a few minutes each week. I wore what I call "Buddy Holly" glasses. They have nothing to do with the late singer other than the frames resemble the ones he wore, and I've been a lifelong fan. Each lens was polarized, essentially allowing through only light waves oriented in one plane: vertically on one side and horizontally on the other. With these glasses, I would look at pictures of Old King Cole, Humpty Dumpty and Little Bo Peep printed on clear plastic. There are two plastic sheets that can slide over each other from left to right. On each sheet are identical images, except that one is vertically polarized and only visible through one lens, and the other is horizontally polarized and can be seen only through the other lens. Another difference is that on one sheet, the King has his pipe, on the other, his bowl. Likewise, Humpty's hat is on one and his cane on the other. And Bo Beep has either her staff or her sheep, but neither sheet has both. The object is to see King Cole with both his pipe and his bowl, and so on. The ability to slide the sheets apart and back together makes the exercise dynamic, and I began to have moments when the images would start to merge. That could only occur if both eyes were working together, even if only for a moment.

For another exercise, I stuck a couple of images on my walls at eye level, a sunfish, say, on one wall and a circle on an adjacent wall. Holding the edge of a small mirror vertically along the bridge of my nose, I would look at the circle with one eye and the sunfish in the mirror. Slowly, by turning the mirror, I would bring the images together in my view. At first, as the images approached each other, one or the other would simply vanish, but with practice, I got better at seeing the sunfish in the circle.

I kept some 3" × 5" cards on my desk with exercises on them. One had two pennies pasted to it, about an

inch apart. I held the card up about a foot away with the
two pennies side-by-side. With my other hand, I held the
tip of a pick-up stick between my nose and the card. By
crossing my eyes and focusing on the tip, I would try to
make the two pennies appear to be three. Like with the
other exercises, it didn't work at first, but eventually I was
able to remove the pick-up stick and continue to see all
three pennies.

Even though I wasn't doing a lot of homework per se,
more of my attention each day was turned to the project.
I simply began focusing on how much of my vision was
coming through my left (non-dominant) eye. I could
certainly see the left periphery, which could only be seen
with my left eye, but I would start observing what else I
was seeing in the foreground as I looked at something else,
near or far. How much of the left lens of my glasses was I
seeing at the same time? My left upper and lower eyelids?
The left side of my nose? And am I still seeing the same on
the right?

And I paid attention to what it took to make this
happen, to increase the vision in my left eye without
suppressing the right. Not surprisingly, the answer wasn't
doing *something*, but the opposite, it was to *not* do all
the things I did to suppress. I had to relax my face and
not attempt to "look" but to just "see." Angela called it
"looking softly." This simple practice of getting my mind to
erase a lifetime of ingrained behavior is at the same time
enormously profound. I was changing my brain with my
mind and persistence!

The increased awareness of what my left eye was seeing
was rewarding in terms of the progress I was making and,

at the same time disturbing. I began seeing double. It wasn't as though there were suddenly two of everything, and oddly, people seemed to be the most common object of duplication. At first, it was the more common appearance of the "floating eye" that I wrote about earlier. But then, people began having two heads, and eventually I started seeing Gina standing beside herself in the doorway. She was merely overlapping, in actual fact.

Prior to vision therapy I'd always assumed, yet with no evidence, that using the wrong prescription or adding unnecessary prisms was potentially harmful. It surprised me to learn that's exactly what I had begun doing, both in the clinic and everywhere else. Mind you, the weird lenses, some with equally strange frames, which I wore at the clinic were beyond anything I wore at home or on the street. In particular, as the emphasis turned to helping my eyes work together and eventually fuse, prisms were part of the effort.

My understanding as a patient, not a professional, is that using prisms in this way really helped me a lot to "dis-attach" my eyes from their habitual ways of working. Although they didn't work together properly, they remained in lockstep. Most often, they operated in parallel. As my right eye turned to follow an object or to read a line of print, my left eye would turn a commensurate amount. That would seem normal if I were watching something move in the distance, but as an object neared my nose, my right eye would turn left toward my nose to follow it, and my left eye would turn left, too, away from my nose. By applying prisms of different powers in varied orientations over one eye or the other, I began to shake up that habitual behavior, and I could actually feel my eyes become more "plastic" in their attachment to each other and their old ways.

An optical prism is basically a transparent wedge that gets more powerful as one edge gets thicker, with power measured in diopters. One diopter of prism will move an apparent image one centimeter on a flat surface one meter away.

An ordinary hard prism is bulky, can be thick on one edge depending upon its power, and is therefore difficult to attach to my glasses. Instead, Dr. Dobson introduced me to Press-On Fresnel prisms from 3M Health Care. These prisms, varying up to several diopters in power, come in flexible clear plastic sheets, can be oriented in any direction, cut with scissors to fit, and will stick to the lens of my glasses with surface tension alone. Fresnel lenses have long been used in lighthouses to focus a relatively small light source so as to be seen for miles at sea. Fresnel lenses consist of several rows of prisms aligned next to each other that act as one big lens or prism. In lighthouse lenses they are typically huge concentric circles of glass prisms. On these Press-On prisms, they are tiny, straight rows. The effect is the same, with little thickness or bulk. They are practically invisible, from inside or out. With the earlier steps, I had been reversing the suppression of my left eye, now I was loosening the ways my eyes had been locked together in the past.

For the first time in my life, I began to tell friends and even select strangers, about my condition and what I hoped to do about it. Another old habit was changing.

28

Mysterious Colored Lights

I mentioned earlier the long funnel at Vision Sense, with a red or green light at the small end, that I sat in a darkened room and stared into for what seemed like eternities. There wasn't much to do during those times, except stare. I occupied my mind by trying, as best I could, to see with both eyes. There's not much to report on that, however, other than the inside of the funnel was slightly rough, and that the light seemed globular sometimes, even though it wasn't. I was doing the exercise because I was asked to, and because I was told it was a valuable part of the therapy, not because I understood how it worked or saw any effect.

That changed when Dr. Dobson gave me glasses to practice with at home. These were cardboard frames with plastic lenses of very particular colors. The first pair had one green lens and one red lens, like the 3D movie glasses of times past (I attended one such movie as a child and saw a blurred double image, either red or green, depending on the eye I chose). As complementary colors, when red and green are combined through fusion of the two visual streams, they create a third different-colored image. Supposedly. I had little success with the first pair, but the next two were different.

This time one pair had two green lenses, the other had two red ones. They weren't just ordinary off-the-shelf colors, either. The red was a deep ruby and the green was like dark grass. Angela instructed me to wear them while I performed "pursuits" with a penlight. First, while wearing the red pair, I would stand and hold the penlight at arm's length, first moving it rapidly up and down a foot or so ten times while I followed it with my eyes, then the same side to side, and finally in-and-out, from my nose to arm's length. I would do the same ten reps of each, sitting cross-legged, and then again lying on my back. I would then repeat the same exercise with the green lenses, following the moving penlight in the dark with my eyes. Inexplicably, my eyes were drawn to the penlight like it was a science fiction tractor beam. And I only saw one light at a time, not two! Previously, when Angela used penlights in the dark, I saw double.

The change was exciting, yet I began to weep. And the more I did these exercises with the glasses and the penlight, the more the tears ran out my eyes and down my cheeks. I wasn't sad, I didn't hurt, and I wasn't crying, but the tears flowed. Strangely, even perversely perhaps, the more the tears came, the more I pressed on, increasing reps to 12 and then 15. I honestly didn't know if what was happening was good or bad, but finally here was something tangible. I could make tears flow by pursuing red and green dots in the dark! Later I'd learn this is called "Asthenopia" or "painful vision," even though I experienced no pain. Asthenopia became a more constant companion as my vision therapy progressed until, one day later on, it would practically disappear.

A great deal of knowledge has been gained about the power of light in healing of various kinds. I know very little about the mechanisms at play, and how light therapy helped my vision remains a mystery. Yet, between the hours I spent peering down the Vision Sense funnel at red and green lights, and the daily penlight pursuits with my colored glasses, light therapy may have been the most powerful modality of all. I understand it the least, so I'll accept it as magic.

Asthenopia became a marker for progress. Throughout the period of my vision training, I walked. And on my walks, I practiced what I called "eye-wareness." I had always had peripheral vision – now I practiced bringing my peripheral vision from both eyes towards the middle.

As my walks continued, the familiar tears of asthenopia would start pouring down my cheeks from both eyes. And as I began each walk my objective was just that, to bring tears to my eyes, because I knew it represented change. I still didn't know what was going on. I suspected that I was using muscles, or awakening muscles that had been sleeping for decades.

29

Neuroplasticity

Since my twenties I'd realized that increasing my self-awareness was a worthy pursuit, yet I only found occasional time for it. But, once the seed was planted, my mind's interest could only grow. By my seventh and eighth decades I had learned to observe my own mind's workings. My work as a life coach was essentially to help others raise their own awareness, and I naturally benefitted from that work as well.

Yet I was not prepared for what I would encounter as I worked on my vision. I would have to find or create an accessible place in my mind where I could encourage it to change decades-old habits of my brain. I needed to find in my mind the "switch" or "dial" that would turn up the vision in my left eye, or more correctly, turn off a lifetime of suppression – not just of one eye, but much more, I would discover.

Neuroplasticity, or the lack of it after the "critical period," was the reason cited since my childhood that I'd never be able to see in 3D.

I hadn't thought of my work with Angela in terms of neuroplasticity, but by coincidence, I read Dr. Norman Doidge's book *The Brain that Changes Itself*, and was so fascinated that I also read *The Brain's Way of Healing*. What I was doing had everything to do with neuroplasticity. And I wasn't the first to defy old beliefs, particularly regarding the possibility of neuroplasticity throughout one's life.

Neuroplasticity is defined as the brain's ability to reorganize itself by forming new neural connections. Neurons, or nerve cells, consist of long, snaky tendrils extending out each way from the cell body. These tendrils and their fingers match up with the tendrils of other neurons, but don't quite touch. Neurotransmitter chemicals, released by the nerve cells in the gaps between them, called synapses, close the connection between neurons, creating pathways. In his books, Dr. Doidge emphasizes that "neurons that fire together, wire together," reinforcing and building these neural pathways. Even in the short period between his writing one book and then the other, large strides had been made in understanding the human capability for neuroplasticity throughout life.

It was originally thought that neuroplasticity was only possible up to five years of age. Today, most optometrists and ophthalmologists still believe that the period of plasticity is less than ten years of age, although it has been shown that neuroplasticity is possible at any age. We now know that a human brain can repurpose unused or underused neurons to help form new pathways or even create new brain cells. I didn't understand the power I had to change my brain when I began vision therapy at 70. Now, with barely a thought, I can "dial in" the level of stereopsis that I desire. Angela had told me that the brain prefers stereopsis and that is proving true.

30

Muscle Memories

Shortly after I began seeing Angela for vision therapy, she suggested that I could benefit from working with Tatiana Reymarova, who had set up a low massage table in the large room behind Angela's offices. She was there two days each week seeing Angela's other patients.

I'd never heard of the Feldenkrais Method, but I was open-minded, and I really wanted to be successful at it. What an experience it was! Tatiana slowly awakened neural pathways between my brain and the left half of my body. Trauma, stored for decades in muscles, mostly on my left side, also woke up. Sometimes I would go from the physical pleasure of the light touch and slow movements to uncontrollable sobbing. Particularly around my eyes, but elsewhere as well, I held pain from my first surgery at three, if not before.

It seems that we store memories of trauma in our muscles or in the neurons that weave among them. Since beginning vision therapy, and especially while working with Tatiana, exercises with certain muscles, particularly my eye muscles, have triggered memories, and with them, emotions.

I also understood how profound the effect of strabismus had been on my entire body. When my brain had decided to turn my left eye toward my nose and weaken its acuity, it didn't have the targeting ability I had credited it with. Instead of shutting down my left eye, my brain had shut down the left half of my body. This began to explain things that had been mysteries for most of my life.

I was already aware that I carried my head turned, and leaned toward the left, bringing my dominant right eye closer to my centerline. I had also attributed neck and shoulder pain to that misorientation and had experimented with eye exercises to relieve the pain, especially when driving.

But I didn't know the extent of my brain's suppression on my body and even my mental state. Neural pathways are either excitatory (those that contract muscles), or inhibitory (those that relax them). Essentially, while the excitatory neural pathways remained operating, constantly telling the muscles on my left side to contract, the inhibitory pathways, which would deliver the message to relax, were shut down. So, the muscles on my left side never rested. I even had to learn with Tatiana how to expand my rib cage when I inhaled. It had been frozen my whole life.

Now the chronic "spastic" left psoas muscle that had given me back and hip pain for years, and the crooked big toe on my left foot made sense. Tatiana pointed out that I had a slight limp that I wasn't even aware of. When I mentioned it to Gina, she said she'd noticed it when we met and thought it was charming. We took Tango lessons and both of us noticed that I had a tendency to pull to the left when we danced. And most amazingly, I realized that the constant contraction of my left side explained why one side of my face grew more than the other, giving me uneven ears and a slanted, but not unpleasant, smile.

31

Waiting to Pop

Susan Barry began vision therapy without the express purpose of becoming stereoscopic. She didn't believe it was possible and, as an academic neurobiologist, had been using herself as an example of permanent strabismus with her students for years. I remembered reading in *Fixing My Gaze* that her unsteady vision was most troublesome when she was driving. What I didn't recall was that her vision had first "popped" – that the steering wheel of her car had stood out in 3D in front of her – after only her second session! I don't know how I missed that fact, but if I had known it, I may not have carried on for almost a year without a pop. I'll count that oversight as a blessing. Angela and I used the word "pop" ourselves, particularly in the early months. Nobody should expect, nor did I, that popping meant sudden and permanent stereopsis. It would merely be a milestone when it occurred.

There was a false pop or two along the way. One time at Angela's clinic, I had been trying unsuccessfully to read a passage with polarized "Buddy Holly" glasses. Suddenly, I could read it clearly, and to our delight, I read it out smoothly and evenly without hesitation. It wasn't until I got home that I realized the lenses had gotten dislodged and slid up in the big frames. I was merely peering beneath them without knowing it. Angela agreed that was what had happened.

The constant change of scenery while driving, like walking, seems to stimulate the neurons I'm trying to change. I've made an effort to maintain "eye-wareness" whenever on the street or the sidewalk. While I may have had my first stereoscopic event on the highway, I'll never be certain. I was looking at a familiar sight: asphalt pavement tapering to a vanishing point on the horizon, grassy banks bordered by dark pines filling in the sides, and a sky filled with puffy clouds above them. Suddenly, and only for a few seconds, the sky seemed to come apart from the trees and move on its own behind them. Then, things returned to normal. Angela thought it might be 3D vision, but wasn't certain, either.

That a simple nail clipper would be the first thing I'd see in 3D seems mundane, but no more so than a steering wheel, I guess. I was clipping my fingernails at my desk where the lighting was good. Suddenly, this simple, chrome-on-steel tool had *shape*. Because my eyes are further apart than the tool is wide, I could see both sides of the clipper at once for the first time! This was it, what I'd been working toward for almost ten months, a pop. I was seeing in 3D! I made a special note of the day.

It's hard to describe the thrill of having something transform in front of my eyes, to have something that had appeared one way all my life, now look different. As I finished cutting my nails, I thrilled in the vision and prayed it wouldn't end. At lunch, the domed silver saltshaker did the same thing, and jumped out at me in vivid 3D. I reveled in the experience, perhaps knowing that it wouldn't last, but was only a teaser, just something to keep me going.

When I reflect on my first pop and Susan Barry's,
I'm not surprised that the thing they have in common
is reflective rounded surfaces, a steering wheel and nail
clippers. Everything we see is reflected light. As I noted
before, light from a distant source reflecting on a near
surface arrives at each eye from slightly different places.
This effect seems to be accentuated on shiny, curved
surfaces like tiles, sink fixtures, and automobiles. I suspect
that the additional stimulus of this effect triggered our
first 3D experiences. It would give me a lot of joy when
stereopsis became a reality, though that wouldn't happen
for many more months – so long that the nail clipper event
seemed like a dream.

32

Reported Sightings

As a year and a half of vision therapy came and went, I found more time and more ways to encourage my eyes to work together as a team. Beyond the exercises I've mentioned, my challenge every waking moment was to ask myself, "how much of what I'm seeing is coming from my left eye?" That continues to be my practice to this day: first the awareness, then the "eye-wareness." It's much more common to find myself already fully stereoptic now, but that has been a gradual process and will remain so for the rest of my life. Other times, I still find myself with my head turned, looking with only one eye!

First visions of 3D seemed ephemeral, like hunting for ghosts. As I mentioned before, motion seemed to stimulate early experiences. Sitting in the Halifax Public Gardens in late summer, watching leaves shimmer in the sun and wind, I had a moment like that. Not only the treetops in the distance but nearby trunks as well seemed to change their form. But it was fleeting and, like when seeing a ghost, I wasn't eager to broadcast my sighting.

After the nail clipper event, I knew that I was capable of seeing in 3D with my own eyes. Susan Barry had been my role model up to that point, but now, seeing with my own eyes had taken things up a notch. I had invested a lot and had developed some helpful habits, and I was determined to see in 3D again. My reward finally came as a Christmas gift, 18 months after I'd begun. By the New Year a week later, I would experience many little stereoscopic events that together shook my world. I was on my way and I wasn't turning back!

There were minor events like walking into my darkened bedroom to see only one red indicator light on the alarm, instead of the two I'd been seeing forever. In the kitchen, I could see both sides of the knife as I sliced with it. Further, I could see both sides of Gina's head when I looked at her, not to mention her indescribable quality of "roundness" or depth. Faucets stuck out at me with their shiny shapeliness.

My hands became a touchstone, a test, that I would use to determine if I was seeing in 3D. I would relax my face and look "softly" as Angela had instructed, and my cupped hands and fingers moving in front of me would take form in three dimensions. The blurry background doubled up, helping to confirm the fusion. For months, whenever I wanted to know if I could still do it, I would look at my hands. They never failed me from then on.

Physical changes began as well. When I looked softly in order to increase the balance and fusion of my eyes, my left eye opened. And each time, it opened a little more. Now, I could not only sense that I was seeing with both eyes, but I could feel my left eye open. I could never have done this with voluntary control. Over time, my face has changed, becoming more balanced, although my left eye still closes more when I smile. One physical change isn't as desirable: often, when using my eyes together for a task, my feet will move involuntarily. I'm not certain the movements are related to my eyes, but I don't recall it happening before.

January and February were full of delightful surprises. I cannot emphasize enough how unprepared I was. I wasn't blind and learning to see; rather, I was stereoblind and learning to see in 3D and experience stereopsis. There is no way to describe the *feeling* I got from seeing the world in its fullness, even if I was only getting glimpses at first.

The feeling of being *inside* something else was new. We have articulated buses in Halifax, two lengthy buses connected into one by bellows. Sitting in the back, watching the bus undulate about me, made me feel like I was riding inside a giant worm.

Crossing a suspension bridge in my car felt entirely different. As I drove on, and I watched the cables rise beside me, I felt enveloped, even embraced, by the structure. Other people may feel that every day, but I doubt it.

Bridges weren't required to sense a new feeling, either. I sometimes felt like I was moving through space differently as I walked through a park or across a room.

Simple things looked very different, too, like a water glass. As I tilted it up to drink, I could see the entire inside! And the outside blew me away. It was totally unexpected, but I realized that previously, I'd been able to see into the glass obliquely from one side or the other, past my nose. Seeing the whole inside was amazing! As for the outside, I don't know what others see, but it certainly wasn't what I expected. It didn't merely appear tubular, but had extra width. Depending on how far along the length I focused, I could move the "fat part" from one end to another. If I looked up close, the end would appear wide and flat-topped. The tricks we can play with a streaming pair of eyes!

When I woke up each morning, I wondered if I still had fusion. I usually looked at my hand, and some days I wasn't certain. But progress was always forward. In January I went to a 3D movie at an IMAX theater. This time, the glasses worked. It was a milestone, but I left wondering why people would go to so much effort and not even come close to what I was now experiencing every day. Even ordinary movies had more depth, a phenomenon I'm not able to explain.

I didn't need to worry about going backward. At times, the stereopsis would be so much in my face as to be a problem, such as when our wisteria needed its winter pruning. Devoid of leaves, but with branches growing every which way, the vine needed to have a few buds removed from the end of each stem. What seemed to happen was that I could see the stem that I was cutting in 3D, but there were two of every other! It was simply too confusing. I wondered then if I would learn to suppress the extra images arising from stereoscopic vision. I had done a similar thing when I had learned to suppress the second image as an infant strabismic.

33

Finding the Switch

*The idea that the brain can change its own structure
and function through thought and activity is, I believe,
the most important alteration in our view of the brain.*
— Norman Doidge, MD,
The Brain that Changes Itself

From the first pop onward, binocular fusion came upon
me involuntarily, often as a surprise. My eventual goal
was to have automatic full-time stereoscopic vision, but I
realized that first I needed to be able to turn it on at will.
I had some clues and cues. Looking "softly," relaxing the
muscles around my eyes and looking at my hands were
among them.

Somehow, if I held my mouth just right, I might find
the switch in my brain. Meanwhile, delights abounded,
even as frustration lingered.

For the first few months, I dictated notable experiences
into my phone. I variously wrote: "I fear that it won't take,"
"Today I can turn it on at any time I want; the challenge
is to remember how to do it again tomorrow," "I'm really
fighting to maintain stereopsis today," and "The joy of
knowing that it is irreversible now, even though some
doubt remains." In addition, I wrote: "I just don't want the
wonder to end!"

I walked a lot, and the tears of asthenopia were my
companion. I wanted to comfort the people who looked at
me with sympathy, to tell them I was happy, but it would
have been pointless. In fact, asthenopia seemed to be the
price I had to pay in order to see outdoors in 3D. I didn't
like it; sometimes the tears blurred my vision, but it was
worth it. Halifax is an old city, and even though it was
leveled by a great explosion 100 years ago, grand old trees
line the sidewalks. Walking among the trees was a great
joy. Not only did I have that feeling of being "inside" the
canopy for the first time, the texture of the bark and the
roundness of the trunk captivated me. A single tree trunk
was an entire world to explore, the ridges and crevasses
like mountains and river valleys, and the moss so rich
in patterns. I was the old guy staring at a tree trunk
and weeping!

Our sidewalks are often straight and appear like long
tunnels, with dwellings lining one side, tree trunks the
other, and crowns overhead. Peering down these tunnels
arose as a challenge at first, but clearly one I wanted to
surmount. This was a way to focus on the "middle," the
place the "battle" had waged all my life. On the 18th of
January, I reported that I could see straight ahead and
hadn't been able to before. Two days later, looking down
the sidewalk took extra effort and produced tears. But
gradually I learned to look way ahead and could watch cars
crossing through the tunnel blocks away, while looking
with both eyes fused together.

I learned the word "proprioception," which is the
sense of where one's body is in space. Try standing with
your eyes closed: Do you know where your arms are?

Do you know if you are standing straight or leaning to one side? I had always felt balanced the way I was, which was decidedly asymmetrical. I'd always stood so that my dominant right eye was on the centerline, facing forward, and I'd walked with an almost imperceptible limp. Now, just as my eyes had needed to "unlock" in order to find new ways to cooperate, my body seemed to be discarding its old feeling of balance so that it could realign. In fact, when I climbed the stairs in the dark, I would lose my balance altogether. This feeling lasted for a while, but I now have a new, more symmetrical stance and stride.

Two forces combined to change my posture. Working with Tatiana had made me more conscious of how I held myself and how I walked. For example, she taught me to lean forward when I wanted to walk, and my feet would follow. To walk faster, lean further. But mostly, I paid more attention to symmetry in pose, and muscle relaxation. The other force was my eyes themselves. The more they worked in unison, the more they drew my head around to the front. I noted the first time I had my hair cut without my head having to be straightened a single time. Usually, my head would return to the same position over and over as I watched the haircut in the mirror with my dominant eye.

When it came to seeing in 3D, mirrors were a real bugaboo, along with computer screens and pages of print. Perhaps I was trying too hard, but to see my own image reflected in 3D seemed nearly impossible. Maybe because the image is optically twice as far away as the mirror frame, my brain resisted seeing a double image of the frame. I don't have a television, but use a computer screen a lot. The screen, like a book, appears flat, so my brain seems to go automatically into flat (one-eyed) mode. It requires a conscious effort to bring both eyes into play. There is a payoff when I do, however. For some reason that I don't understand, when I am looking with both eyes at a movie the images on the flat screen appear to have depth they didn't have before!

Three other challenges that remained long past the first few months of 3D vision were the floating third eye, the Brock string, and being indoors, in general. Small rooms seem to present a particular challenge. Perhaps it's because everything is far enough away to appear in two places, yet close enough to present a real conflict, particularly when I'm surrounded by walls. My eyes seem to revert to the easiest way of seeing. Angela told me once that the eyes favor stereopsis, and that has proven to be true in the long run, but for me the change has been very gradual.

Color came as a total surprise. I hadn't expected my perception of color to change, but it did. Flower blossoms were a delight. They not only had intricate shapes and depth that I'd never observed before, but their colors appeared brighter and more vivid. I had expected 3D vision as a result of getting my brain to process the information from both eyes at once. What I had not expected was that my brain would take the color that each eye saw and add them together in my brain, making the colors more vivid.

As I developed the ability to get my brain to "fuse" the vision streams from my eyes, I noticed two additional phenomena. I began to "lead with the left." While it sounds like a boxing term, my left eye was the weak one and had always been the follower, yet now it led. At first, it was by intention, but I found my left eye leading on its own. When I moved my eyes to glance in a new direction or to follow a moving object, my left eye led the way.

I noticed, too, that when I was moving my eyes, they didn't move smoothly, but seemed to jerk around in tiny, rapid motions along the way. At times it seemed like the fusion was intermittent, first one eye, then the other, as these jerky movements occurred several times a second. Moving pictures are actually still photos shown at 60 frames per second, so why couldn't stereoscopic vision work the same way? I haven't pursued that hypothesis, but these movements, called "saccades" are perfectly normal, and we just don't notice them because they are so rapid.

The sum of these discoveries was a growing sense that I could find the "switch" more reliably all the time. I didn't have a map to that place in my mind, but like any other "muscle" I was learning to control 3D vision and stereopsis with my intention. Now it was time to see new things.

34

Vision Quest

Gina had never been to the American Southwest, and I immediately recognized that its broad landscapes and skies would provide me with the panoramic views I'd been craving. I'd always known the West as "Big Sky Country" but hadn't previously had the means to see it all at once. Halifax and Nova Scotia are beautiful, but unless you get into a boat and head offshore, there are few places that offer a wide-open view to the horizon. I needed that view in order to grow.

We began our journey in Phoenix, Arizona. As fate would have it, Dr. Robin Lewis, a respected leader in vision therapy, would be in town and available for dinner. That's how my vision quest began, at a Mexican restaurant in Tempe, facing enchiladas and an imposing grey-haired teacher with a runaway mustache.

Dr. Dobson had graciously arranged for me to meet Robin and his vision therapy colleague, Dr. John Abbondanza, for dinner at a Halifax Mexican restaurant barely a month earlier. They were using her facility to train local optometrists in vision therapy. That dinner had opened the door for my visit in Phoenix.

Robin was born to teach. Despite my superior age, I felt like a student who'd wanted to show my new teacher how bright and informed I was – yet failed to impress.

While we ate, I learned that I didn't really have monocular vision, as I had thought: "You have peripheral vision in both eyes, right?" Robin asked. After we established that, he gave a name and description to the weeping that I had been experiencing to a disturbing degree: *Asthenopia,* or "painful vision." A "part-time strabismic" himself, his perspective on several things resonated with me.

At Robin's office the next morning, he put me right to work looking through a three-inch diameter magnifying lens through one eye while the other was unobstructed. A truck in the parking lot would look a fraction of the size of its counterpart beside it. And he would get me to stretch my ability to change how I saw what I saw.

"Just look," he would say, his version of Angela's "look softly." And I felt like I was looking differently, like looking through my own vision, if there is such a thing.

More than any optometrist I'd ever met, he reinforced in me the lesson that my vision is in my brain!

And he taught me about Jump Duction. I loved the name before I knew what it was. And once Robin explained the premise, I was interested in trying it.

I wanted to wean my eyes from the prism I'd been wearing. The left lens had been ground to incorporate a 3-diopter prism into my already-strong prescription. The prism bent the light coming into my eye in such a way that it compensated for the inward and upward turn of my left eye, moving its image into alignment with my right.

Once my left eye strengthened to the point that it was ready to work with its partner, the prism had allowed it to do so without correcting the actual eye cross.

Now, I wanted to remove the turn from my eye. I was tired of being cross-eyed. One approach was to apply an equal and opposite prism. In this instance, because my left lens included a 3-diopter prism with the base (the thick edge) to the lower left, I used a 6-diopter prism with the base opposite, to the upper right. Fusion now required my left eye to move twice as far as it would have, with no prism at all. "Stretching" in this way would make my eyes feel more comfortable without a prism ultimately. Strangely, now that I have reliable fusion, 3D always seems more vivid in jump duction than normal.

Jump duction worked. Less than three months after Robin Lewis had introduced the concept, and two years after beginning vision therapy, I replaced my left lens with a new one with no prism. Now, when my eyes fused on an object, they really were aligned properly, and not aided by optics. My second goal would also be met: I was not only learning to see in 3D, but I was un-crossing my eyes.

From the time that we left his office that morning, I experienced a sharp reduction in asthenopia, specifically weeping, although it returns in certain circumstances. I don't know what changed: perhaps it only needed a name to fade away.

We spent the next week touring the American Southwest by car, there being no better place for a recovering strabismic! "Panoramic" took on a new meaning for me. For the first time I not only could see forward with both eyes, but now I could see the entire vista, from edge to edge! It was as if I had discovered a new, second way of seeing – everything at once, not in pieces as it had always been. Stereoscopic vision, to someone who has never experienced it, is more than seeing. With it comes a whole new feeling of having a world around me, of being included in it, and it being more alive and fluid. The greatest challenge of this book is to describe seeing in one way to someone who has always seen in another.

On the way back to Nova Scotia, we visited my daughter and her family in Florida. On a previous visit, while in the early stages of my vision therapy, I had attended one of my grandson's baseball games and watched the game through a chain-link fence. The thick wire links got in the way of my vision, just as I would have expected. The game was difficult to see because it was broken into diamond-shaped segments with blind spots between. Yet the effect was the same regardless of which eye I used.

This time, the fence wires seemed to dissolve into what could be more like a fly's-eye view with the diamond-shaped images blending edge-to-edge until it was more like looking through a veil or a screen. I could see the entire game in a way I hadn't imagined.

Standing on my daughter's eighth-floor balcony later that day, watching the Florida sunset, and finally able to take in with my eyes the vast panorama, I thought: "This is the greatest accomplishment of my life." Yet, I asked myself: "Why?" And, as my eyes merged their images together in my brain, my entire body seemed also to coalesce, and for the first time I knew the answer: "Now I can be whole!"

35

Back to the Beginning

Nine months after starting vision therapy and still almost a month before I first saw the nail clippers in 3D, I had written to Sue Barry. I received a warm reply, encouraging me to continue. We stayed in touch and she invited me to visit her if I was ever in her area. That would be my next trip.

We met at her home where she introduced me to her astronaut husband and took me for a tour of beautiful Mount Holyoke College in Massachusetts, from which she had recently retired. Over dinner and afterwards, we spoke at length about strabismus and all that she had learned. Sue has had a profound influence on many strabismics around the world, and even on the science of neuroplasticity. David Hubel, one of the scientists who had promoted the "critical period" theory became a big supporter of hers.[8]

The visit was enjoyable and an interesting contrast. Despite the challenges of strabismus, she had excelled in science and academia. And interesting from my perspective, she was clearly a person with admirable willpower. I know it had taken persistence for me to get

---

8 Steven Gallop, *A Parent Guide to Strabismus, Eye Muscle Surgery & Vision Therapy* (Santa Ana: Optometric Extension Foundation Program, 2014), 20–21

this far, but when she told me that she did eye exercises every day, and was always inventing new ones, my immediate reaction was to stop doing anything. That darned rebel in me! I would learn that she was correct, but that I didn't have to match her effort. Eventually, I returned to using my syntonic eyeglasses and penlight each morning for a few months. When I stopped that, I began carrying a prism around that I could easily slip onto my glasses for a little jump duction while I walk.

Dr. Theresa Ruggiero, Susan's optometrist and vision therapist, was also kind enough to join me for dinner. Little by little, I was learning more about my condition and its treatment. Mostly, I've learned to leave the science up to the experts. Dr. Ruggiero wanted to make one point though: that achieving 3D vision requires a lot of motivation.

Since that time, my vision has progressed steadily. Stereopsis is more often the default state, and I realize that although I will never see like a stereoscopic "native," I may have the best of both worlds, the precision of a single eye, with 3D on demand!

36

Broken Wings

When I moved to Nova Scotia 50 years ago, I gave up
flying. The nearest airport was more than an hour away,
and I was busy raising a family and building boats. A
couple of notable exceptions to my flight hiatus happened
in the Canadian Arctic, where I had found a market
for boats among the Inuit communities. Johnny May,
a renowned bush pilot, invited me to ride along in his
De Havilland Beaver while he delivered a hunter and his
gear to a remote camp. On the return trip, he let me fly
that classic plane from the right seat, listening to the big
radial engine pull us through the cold northern air.

"Air Maybe" was the nickname for the "scheduled"
airline flying De Havilland Twin Otters between Northern
Quebec communities. The aircraft were very reliable
and the pilots, mostly young men on their way to larger
airlines, were good. The weather changed often, and might
be quite different in one place than it was a few miles away,
causing schedules to be unreliable. One fine day, I found
myself the only passenger on a flight, and when the pilot
offered to exchange seats, I jumped at the opportunity.
Besides a few gentle Dutch rolls, I flew straight and level
for the duration and was back in my seat for the landing.
From then on, I always sat in the back when I flew, and my
love of aviation went back to sleep.

Fifty years later, though, it awoke again as a total surprise. I watched a bush plane video, then another. Virtually unchanged over my lifetime, the perennial, fabric-covered taildragger I spotted swordfish with 50 years ago was beginning a renaissance, as oversized and under-inflated tires were opening new areas to aviation. Standing up to three feet in diameter, and inflated at a very low four PSI, the tires allowed planes to land on rocks the size of grapefruits, or just about anywhere. Also called "conventional gear aircraft," taildraggers had become a rarity. Instead of having modern tricycle gear, with a steerable front wheel, which keeps the plane level while taxiing, taildraggers have two main wheels ahead of the center of gravity and a small tailwheel. They are most recognizable on the ground where they sit with their noses in the air, which their pilots cannot see over, and must look through side windows while taxiing.

It all flowed back, and I wanted to fly. I asked myself, "why not?" My kids had kids of their own and I'd long since retired. And most of all, my eyes would not be a problem, now that I could see in 3D. My license only needed a current medical certificate to be valid, and I thought that I could pass. So, watching videos turned into looking in the want ads. And one day, I got a call-back, and I bought Dolly that day, and sent a deposit right away.

Dolly was a 1946 Cessna 140, built exactly 40 days before I was born. It had been entirely restored a few years back, and the 85-horsepower engine boosted to 100. The Cessna had even won the People's Choice Award at the Oshkosh air show one year. It was the price of a car and I decided to put my ten percent down. I was in love. It was February, and the airplane was snowbound in its hangar at a grass strip in Ontario. I couldn't get at it until Spring, so I had until then to bring my license up to date.

Dolly's owner had been a Certified Flight Instructor for 20 years and had owned the airplane for 28 of its 73 years. Because he had a waiting list of willing buyers, he allowed me to make my purchase conditional on passing my medical by spring thaw.

When my medical exam came up on April 4, I passed the 3D vision test with ease. Unfortunately, my blood pressure was high and there was concern about noise from my carotid arteries. Both could be remedied, but they would take time.

After thinking about my dilemma for ten days, I decided that I would buy the airplane, put it in a hangar, and keep working on my medical at my leisure. I opened my computer to send the confirmatory message, only to find this email: "I am very sorry to tell you that my aircraft was severely damaged while taxiing... I will send you back the deposit...immediately. With regrets...."

In what can only be described as a fluke, a gust of wind had lifted the tail just as a wheel had caught up on a chunk of ice, and somersaulted the plane over its nose and onto its back. Its wings and propeller bent, its tail crushed, and the engine would have to be torn down and rebuilt. The owner's perfect record and my dream of owning Dolly were both smashed.

I carried on for another year, got my blood pressure under control and actually elected for surgeries to "quiet" my noisy carotid arteries, reducing the risk of stroke. Despite that work, and my incredibly improved vision, a medical certificate and my license to fly remain beyond my grasp, and I've halted the pursuit. I'll have to earn my next wings in Heaven.

Long Live the Wonder!

Since my first glimpses in 3D, I've felt two powerful desires which in fact may be mutually exclusive. One wish is that the wondrous delight that I get from 3D vision never ends, that it never be commonplace. Paradoxically, I want it to be as ordinary as opening my eyes.

Three years have passed since the Christmas I had daily experiences of 3D vision. It has been a gradual process and there have been new delights and discoveries along the way.

I am now seeing in 3D with my eyes straight and working together naturally. I believe that I have achieved most of my potential to fully experience this, perhaps the greatest of the five senses. There may be new surprises, and I hope that the wonder will never end. Nonetheless, I remain a work in progress. I will continue in my own flawed way to fight the other battles in my life as well. But in this one I can truly *see* victory!

Twenty years ago, early in my coaching career, I developed two aphorisms for my life. One is "I'll be there at the end, and I'll have all I need to get there." It has reminded me that, knowing death is inevitable, there is nothing to fear in the meantime, and I needn't be rich to achieve it. I did not expect to reach the most optimistic goal I've ever dared, which is "to see in 3D before I die."

The other aphorism is "Only good things happen to me, and sometimes they're opportunities to learn." It took a long time to find the goodness in strabismus, but now, after a lifetime of stereoblindness, I understand the gift of 3D vision! And I have learned to use the inherent plasticity of my brain and the power of my mind to change the way I see. With the rare perspective of having seen both ways, I hope some of my lessons can help others.

In Hindsight

Cancer

I'd had prostate cancer for five years when I asked Doctor
Dobson to help me see in 3D. I had already survived the
disease a year longer than my father, who had endured
every procedure the medical community suggested
and sought alternative care abroad as well. After much
consideration, I'd chosen a different route, eschewing
anything that I deemed an assault on my immune system,
like radiation, surgery or chemotherapy, along with
unnecessary imaging. If having a scan would not change
my action, why expose myself?

I've had the good fortune to have friends recommend
a few wonderful healers, invariably teachers themselves,
who have helped me to improve my health, and to slow
and, sometimes reverse, the course of the disease. It's been
twelve years now, I'm closer to the end, yet more grateful
for the gifts of life than ever.

Critical Period

I use the term "critical period" throughout this book,
although it may have been coined in the early 1960s. The

belief that fusion couldn't be achieved after a certain age was not new when I was young, and it persists today. I asked Susan Barry if she could clarify the history for me and she sent this wonderful reply:

> As for your question concerning age and fusion, Claud Worth in 1903 published a very influential book titled *Squint: Its Causes, Pathology, and Treatment.* He studied 2300 children with infantile strabismus and found that most, even after surgery, never developed stereopsis. So he concluded that these children were born with a congenital weakness of the fusion faculty. In 1939, Francis Bernard Chavasse, one of Worth's students, published later editions of *Squint* and stated that children with infantile strabismus could develop fusion but only if they were operated on before age two. This is what most ophthalmologists still believe. So when Hubel and Wiesel, in the 1960s, described critical periods, it fit with Chavasse's conclusions. See page 135 of *Fixing My Gaze.*

What Vision Therapy Experts Say

Strabismus Surgery

As I mentioned from the outset, I am not a professional, but a patient. I speak only with one voice about eye surgery and behavior. I hope you will read the words of two vision therapists and authors who have kindly allowed me to share their wisdom. Their books are available from www.oepf.org.

Every parent likely agonizes when an ophthalmologist recommends eye surgery for their child's vision problems. They will think about the pain and trauma that their child will probably experience – physically, mentally and emotionally, especially younger children who don't understand what's happening. Further, parents themselves will naturally feel distressed at the thought of their child suffering.

However, not all eyecare professionals agree with the use of surgery to correct strabismus. Vision therapists believe that the eye muscles are very rarely the cause of vision problems; and therefore, recommend visiting a Developmental or Behavioral Optometrist to better understand the vision process before deciding. Many eye-teaming problems can be corrected through non-surgical means.

Dr. Steven Gallop, a behavioral optometrist, has outlined the potential problems with surgery in his book, *A Parent Guide to Strabismus, Eye Muscle Surgery and Vision Therapy.* The following passages on eye muscle surgery highlight a number of the concerns of Gallop and other colleagues in his field.[9]

Why Eye Muscle Surgeries?
- Eye muscle surgery for strabismus is the second most common eye surgery performed.
- The primary concern of eye muscle surgeons tends to be the cosmetic alignment of the eyes, not the overall function and development of the visual process.
- One or more eye muscles may be repositioned to alter the cosmetic alignment of the eyes. Some surgeons prefer to operate on the problematic eye, some on the other eye; some will operate on both eyes.
- While the quality and safety of these procedures has improved over the years, there has been little change in the philosophy of most surgeons who are diagnosing and treating these conditions, and therefore little change in the quality of the outcomes.
- This surgery-based philosophy presumably maintains that there is some problem with the eye muscles when the two eyes are not aiming properly. While eye muscle damage can actually happen, it is quite rare. Many people experience less than satisfactory results after

---

9 Steven Gallop, *A Parent Guide to Strabismus, Eye Muscle Surgery & Vision Therapy* (Santa Ana: Optometric Extension Foundation Program, 2014), 20–21

surgery because of the limitations of this philosophy. Problems may surface immediately following the operation or may take several years to become noticeable. At this point, I'm referring to eye alignment problems. There is absolutely no guarantee that eyes which appears straight immediately after surgery will stay that way.

• Surgery to straighten the eyes is based on the assumption that realigning the eyes so they will appear straight to an outside observer will fix everything. I have examined hundreds of people who would be candidates for eye muscle surgery. More and more parents tell me the surgeon said there was nothing wrong with their child's eye muscle(s), but surgery on the healthy muscles is the only way to straighten the eyes. These parents were completely bewildered by this pronouncement, as I am – though it seems like a step in the right direction for the surgeons to acknowledge this. Most surgeons still believe that most poorly aligned eyes are due to faulty muscles as far as I can tell. Again, even if this was true, the overall thinking is still problematic due to the lack of accounting for the complexity of the visual process.

Multiple eye surgeries and complications

• The need for multiple operations is quite common. Many people have unsatisfactory results from eye muscle surgery because the eyes are merely part of an intricate visual process that mostly occurs in the brain.

• When a surgically straightened eye deviates again, surgeons simply see this as an indication of the need for further surgery. Actually, the need for multiple operations is quite common when the standard medical/surgical approach is taken.

- Unfortunately, because of differing philosophes, all of these people must continue with their vision as it is or attempt further surgery unless they are fortunate enough to find a doctor who understands their problems from a different perspective. They need a doctor who knows how to work with them to achieve improvement through non-surgical means – a behavioral optometrist.

- The prevalence of reoperations is so great that most of the literature and numerous websites featuring strabismus FAQs mentioned the need for multiple surgeries very matter-of-factly, and a great number of articles had the word "reoperation" in the title . Apparently it is not considered a negative factor if an individual should need multiple procedures. I find it stunning that surgeons can be satisfied with eyes being straight "at any time" after the surgery. Apparently they are not concerned with how long the eyes remain straight, just that they look straight for even a moment.

- Proof of the prevalence of the surgical way of thinking is demonstrated by one of the most significant advances in these procedures, the principles of which have remained essentially unchanged since the mid-19th century when this surgery was first done – adjustable sutures. This technique so blatantly admits the uncertainty surrounding eye muscle surgery as to be beyond the obvious, verging on the absurd. This procedure provides for an adjustment to be made a day or so after the surgery has been "completed," if it is felt that some fine tuning is in order. One other innovation which appeared around the same time (the late 1970s) was Botulinum toxin injection, used to create a partial paralysis of the eye muscle(s) this requires an injection of the toxin into the particular muscle or muscles that supposedly need weakening.

Replacing Surgery with Vision Therapy

• One thing we do know is that the visual process is not an eye process; it is a brain and body process. The visual process is pervasive in human behavior and development. The eyes themselves are fairly complex structures, but their main purpose is to absorb light and convert that light into chemical signals, which then become electrical signals that travel to and from many parts of the brain and body. It is important to think in terms of seeing with our brains rather than with our eyes.

• The crossed eye is not the real problem. The real problem is the brain's inability to integrate and coordinate the two eyes. Realigning an eye only addresses the symptom – a cosmetic abnormality. Vision therapy is the best way to keep the eyes straight and working together.

• Many people considered candidates for eye muscle surgery have managed to overcome their visual problems non-surgically, or have found higher level improvement by adding vision therapy to other treatments.

- I was also taken aback at the ease with which they seem ready to do surgery all over again however many times it takes, completely ignoring the permanent damage to the muscle(s) caused by each procedure. I know I have made the point repeatedly that the visual process is one that mostly occurs in the brain, but that does not negate the need for healthy, fully functioning eye muscles, able to carry out the instructions from the brain effortlessly, instantaneously, and accurately. None of this is ever quite the same once an eye muscle has been damaged – surgically or otherwise. Vision therapy after eye muscle surgery can often be very successful, but the permanent and substantial restriction of normal muscle function that results from the scar tissue, and the destruction of the special fibers telling the brain where the eye is pointing, makes everything more difficult.

And here's more wisdom from another vision therapist and author, Dr. Pilar Vergara Giménez:

- If, after careful consideration, you select surgery for yourself or for a child, then optometric vision therapy should be performed pre- and post-operatively. The pre-surgical vision therapy is designed to develop peripheral fusion, the "glue" that holds the eyes together. The post-surgical therapy further develops the glue so that the results of surgery have a better possibility of lasting.[10]

---

10 For more information, see the book, *Crossed & Lazy Eyes: Myths, Misconceptions and Truths* by Dr. Pilar Vergara Giménez.

Signs, Symptoms and Behaviors Resulting from Vision Problems

Many adults with vision problems, or parents of strabismic children, are unaware of the multiple signs, symptoms and behaviors that are potentially linked to vision problems. Some are reduced or eliminated once the vision problems are corrected. The following list[11] is not meant to be exhaustive, rather it is intended to help parents and loved ones understand the many complications that may arise due to vision problems:

* Blurry vision
* Eye rubbing
* Eyes that turn in or out
* Gets close to paper when writing
* Eyes tire after reading
* Moves head while reading
* Uses finger to follow words when reading
* Loses place while reading, or skips line
* Doesn't comprehend what they read
* Short attention span
* Mixes up words with similar beginnings
* Difficulty recognizing letters, words or simple shapes
* Difficulty telling the difference between the main idea and less important details
* Difficulty learning math, including size, quantities and proportions

---

11 Sources: Dr. Steven Gallop, Dr. Pilar Vergara Giménez and www.visiontherapy.org

- Difficulty picturing what has been read
- Careless writing and drawing
- Inability to stay on the line when writing
- Poor copying ability
- Can respond visually, but not graphically
- Mixes up "left" and "right"
- Reverses letters, numbers and words
- Difficulty remembering and writing letters and numbers
- Covers one eye with hand, or squints near work
- Complains that letters or words run together
- May describe seeing letters and words "float" on the page
- Procrastinates (starting with homework)
- Poor concentration
- Complains about their eyes, even when they do well with an eye exam
- Reverses letters or numbers often (e.g.: b versus d, z versus s)
- Poor reading fluency; "choppy reader"
- Appears bright yet does poorly on tests
- Misaligns digits in columns
- Transposes numbers or words (e.g.: was/saw or 512/251)
- Difficulty copying from chalkboard or from paper to paper
- Avoids reading
- Spells words phonetically
- Seems visually distracted
- Writes uphill or downhill
- Difficulty with puzzles

- Complains of car sickness or motion sickness
- Diagnosed with ADD, ADHD, dyslexia
- Described as lazy, unmotivated, "acting out," a bully, anxious, agitated

Acknowledgments

I could never have written this book on my own. There would have been no subject matter without Susan Barry's inspiration and Angela Dobson's knowledge and patience. Thank you.

I've had wonderful editors. The book would not have gotten past the first few chapters if it weren't for Gina Brown, my wife, an author and publisher, as luck would have it. She could see that I was blocked and jumped in to help me. She sat by my side as we edited what I had written, and I told my story, often unable to resist the tears. Neither of us realized how painful the process would be. Thank you for holding me, Gina.

Three others read my finished (or so I thought) manuscript, Angela Dobson, OD, refreshed memories and provided her notes from my visits, Susan Barry, PhD, read my manuscript two or three times, helping me get my facts right, and Robin Lewis, OD, helped me to better understand the binocular brain and brought about a worthwhile revision. Their encouragement and generosity have overwhelmed me. Thank you.

Elizabeth Peirce applied her experience, wisdom and subject matter knowledge to proofreading, suggesting valuable improvements and removing an ocean of commas.

To photographer Michael Fuller, thanks, you are the best. And kudos to designer Peggy Issenman with Peggy & Co. Design, for pulling together the creative elements.

Steven Gallop, OD, and Pilar Vergara Giménez, OD, have generously contributed excerpts from their books.

Theresa Ruggiero, OD, and John Abbondanza, OD took the time to consult with me for this book. Thank you very much.

I am grateful to my children and their two families, Rigel Crockett, Ariel Janzen and their daughter, Zella Crockett; and Laurel Crockett Rector, her husband Drew Rector and their son, Luke Rector. Seeing them in 3D is reward enough. And to the Brown Family, Christina, Dale, Tanya and the Muirs, Reisa, Al and Connor, who have become my family in Nova Scotia.

I've also been encouraged, inspired and supported along my journey by others, some of whom have passed. They include Michael Adzich, Patrick Casey, MD, Monique Cupryn, OD, Howard Dutton, Paul Empey, Karen Forrest, John Frediani, Peter Goddard, MD, Mary Hanna, MD, Lora Hurley, ND, Jessica Jennings, DC, Gordon Kyle, Lyn Lewis, Tom Lynch, Lawrence MacDonald, OD, Lisa Martell, Johnny May, Pat McHugh, Trent Palmer, Mike Patey, MJ Patterson, Tatiana Reymarova, Linda Sanet, Richard Sorkin, OD, Parker Vanderhoof, Bill Wiesner and Frank Wiewel. Thank you all! And to anyone I have failed to mention, I am both grateful and regretful.

Glossary

Amblyopia: The visual condition in which there is a low or reduced central visual acuity that cannot be corrected by traditional refractive means (glasses or contact lenses) and which is not attributable to disease, injury, or pathology. According to Ciuffreda, binocular competition in an amblyopic patient causes adaptations to be made via neural suppression, leading to reduced visual acuity and dysfunctions in such skills as ocular motility, fixation, accommodation, spatial sense, and speed of perception in the amblyopic eye.

Astigmatism: The refractive condition in which the light rays from an object are not brought to a single point focus at the back of the eye. Astigmatism is compensated for by the use of lenses with cylinder.

Attention Deficit Disorder (ADD)/Attention Deficit Hyperactivity Disorder (ADHD): Similar to hyperkinetic disorder of the neurodevelopmental type in which the child may be hyperactive, act impulsively or have difficulties maintaining attention. These symptoms begin between ages six and twelve and must be present for more than six months for a diagnosis to be made.

Behavioral optometry: An expanded area of professional optometric practice that uses a holistic approach to the treatment of vision, and vision information processing problems. Behavioral optometry emphasizes the use of lenses, prisms, filters, syntonics and optometric visual therapy to improve the way a patient uses his or her brain to control their eyes and vision, rather than simply prescribe lenses to compensate for weakness in eyesight.

Blind spot: An area on each retina where the optic nerve leaves the eye that contains no photoreceptors and therefore provides no light reception.

Cornea: Transparent structure forming the anterior part of the eye.

Critical period: A phase in development during which an organism has heightened sensitivity to external stimuli that are necessary for the development of a particular skill. It was once believed that if the organism does not receive the appropriate stimulus during this critical period, it may be difficult, ultimately less successful, or even impossible, to develop that skill. More recently a better term, sensitive period, is now being used to describe this period in life, because it is now known that this period is only sensitive, not critical in that the brain is plastic throughout life, and that partial or total recovery can be possible at any age.

Diplopia: The state in which a single object appears as if it were double.

Lazy eye: The colloquial term for amblyopia; however, scientific evidence has shown that the eye is not lazy. The continued use of this term leads to misunderstanding and less effective treatment.

Neuron: A neuron is a specialized cell in the nervous system designed to rapidly communicate with other neurons and organs by sending chemical and electrical signals from one to the other. Neurons help the various parts of the brain to communicate with each other, and allows the brain to communicate back and forth with the body.

Neuroplasticity: The brain's ability to reorganize itself by changing the strength of neural pathways and/or by forming new neural connections. This process is known to continue throughout life.

Occlusion: Blocking sight in one eye through the use of patches and filters. Occlusion may be carried out in many forms; total, partial, graded, bi-nasal, bi-temporal, and spot.

Ophthalmology: The medical specialty that deals with diseases of the eye and eye surgery.

Optician: An optician is a practitioner who fabricates, fits, and dispenses lenses for the correction of a person's vision. In some countries, opticians are also licensed to perform refractions and other duties related to eye examinations.

Optometry: Optometry is a licensed health care profession concerned with the health of the eyes and related structures, as well as vision, visual systems, and vision information processing in humans. Optometrists use lenses, prisms, filters, occlusion, syntonic phototherapy, and optometric vision therapy to rehabilitate and enhance human performance.

Patch: The material used to occlude or block vision in an eye.

Peripheral vision: Vision that comes from areas outside the central foveal area.

Phototherapy (Syntonics): Therapy applied through the use of different frequencies of light to affect changes in vision.

Prism: An optical device that bends light.

Sensory fusion: Neural process by which the two different retinal images coming from each eye are merged (fused) into a single perception.

Stereopsis: The binocular appreciation of depth due to retinal disparity. The eyes are separated in the horizontal plane of the head and each eye has a slightly horizontal disparate view of the world. The sensory fusion of these horizontally disparate unequal retinal images results in three-dimensional perception.

Strabismus (squint, tropia, crossed eyes, wall eyes): The visual condition in which binocular (bi-foveal) fixation is not present. When strabismus is present (manifest) the visual axes of the eyes are not directed toward the same object at the same time.

Suppression: An active (not passive) cortisol process in which the image from one eye is ignored when both eyes are simultaneously stimulated. The main purpose of suppression is to secure a single vision where it would not be attainable otherwise.

Torticollis: The contraction of the neck muscles that causes twisting of the neck and abnormal head position.

Visual acuity (VA): Clarity or sharpness of sight. The ability to see the details of an object. In the USA, it is usually represented as a fraction, which identifies the size of the smallest letters resolved at the testing distance used. The numerator (top number) represents the disk testing distance used, typically 20 feet. The denominator (bottom number) has to do with the size of the letter read. For example: 20/20 means that the individual is able to resolve the letter on the 20/20 line of the Snellen chart at 20 feet.

Visual confusion: The condition in strabismus where each of the two foveas receives an image of a different object. If these images are not suppressed, and correspondence is normal, the patient will perceive the 2 objects as superimposed.

Visual cortex: The area of the brain located in the occipital lobe of the cerebral cortex which is responsible for processing visual information.

Vision therapy: Vision therapy should be prescribed when a comprehensive eye examination indicates that it is an appropriate treatment option for the patient.

The specific program of vision therapy is based on the results of standardized tests, the need of the patient, and the patient's signs and symptoms. Optometric vision therapy programs typically involve the use of lenses, prisms, filters, occluders, specialized instruments and procedures, and/or computer-based programs to rehabilitate and/or enhance visual function in human performance. Vision therapy has been shown to be effective in the rehabilitation and treatment of the following conditions: amblyopia, strabismus, eye movement and focusing disorders, convergence insufficiency, learning-related vision problems, attentional and concentration difficulties, vision problems secondary to traumatic brain injury, strokes and sports vision enhancement.

Glossary excerpts are courtesy of Dr. Pilar Vergara Giménez, from her book *Crossed & Lazy Eyes: Myths, Misconceptions and Truths.*

Bibliography

Abbondanza, John. Interview by author, Framingham, Mass. May 21, 2018.

Barry, Susan. *Fixing My Gaze: A Scientist's Journey into Seeing in Three Dimensions.* New York: Basic Books, 2010.

Barry, Susan. Interview by author, South Hadley, Mass. May 22, 2018.

Benoit, Robin and Jillian Benoit. *Dear Jillian: Vision Therapy Changed My Life Too.* Dallas: Brown Books Small Press, 2013.

Bridge, Concord-Carlisle High School Yearbook, 1964.

Dobson, Angela. Interviews by author, Halifax, Nova Scotia. 2016–2018.

Doidge, Norman. *The Brain that Changes Itself: Stories of Personal Triumph from the Frontiers of Brain Science.* New York: Penguin Books, 2007.

Doidge, Norman. *The Brain's Way of Healing: Remarkable Discoveries and Recoveries from the Frontiers of Neuroplasticity.* New York: Viking, 2015.

Gallop, Steven. *A Parent Guide to Strabismus, Eye Muscle Surgery & Vision Therapy.* Santa Ana: Optometric Extension Foundation Program, 2014.

MacDonald, Lawrence W. *The Collected Works of Lawrence W. MacDonald, V.1 1954–1965.* Santa Ana: Optometric Extension Program, 1992.

Press, Leonard J. *Applied Concepts in Vision Therapy.* Santa Ana: Optometric Extension Program Foundation Edition, 2008.

Ruggiero, Theresa. Interview by author, Northhampton, Mass. May 23, 2019

Sacks, Oliver, MD. "Stereo Sue." *The New Yorker,* June 19, 2006: 64.

Taub, Marc B. and Schnell, Pamela H. *Vision Therapy: Success Stories from Around the World.* Timonium, Maryland: Optometric Extension Program Foundation, Inc., 2016.

Vergara Giménez, Pilar. *Crossed & Lazy Eyes: Myths, Misconceptions and Truths.* Timonium, Maryland: Optometric Extension Program Foundation, Inc., 2016. (Note: also available in Spanish).

In Spanish

Vergara Giménez, Pilar. *Tanta inteligencia tan poco rendimiento* (loosely translated: *So much Intelligence, so Little Performance*). Zaragoza, Espagne. Editorial Aurum Volatile, 2019.

Resources

British Association of Behavioural Optometrists
(BABO – UK)
www.babo.co.uk

Dr. Susan Barry
www.stereosue.com

College of Optometrists in Vision Development (COVD)
www.covd.org

College of Syntonics in Optometry (CSO)
www.csovision.org

Angela Dobson, OD
http://vision-sense.ca

Feldenkrais Method
https://feldenkrais.com

Lazy Eye
www.lazyeye.org (note, this is part of www.optometrists.org)

Robin Lewis, OD
http://www.familyoptometry.net

Optometric Extension Program Foundation (OEPF)
www.oepf.org

Pilar Vergara Giménez, OD
www.pilarvergara.es

Steven Gallop, OD
https://vision-therapy-pa.com

Richard Sorkin, OD
www.saintpetersburgoptometrist.com

Strabismus
www.strabismus.org (note, this is part of
www.optometrists.org)

Vision Therapy
www.visiontherapy.org
www.covd.org
www.visiontherapycanada.com

Index

3D Vision, ix, xii, 3–8, 18–20,
    22, 29, 80, 83, 87, 89, 96, 99,
    103–109, 111–114, 117, 119,
    120, 122, 123, 125, 126, 127,
    140. *See* also Stereopsis and
    Stereoscopic

Alternator, 12, 74, 75
Amblyopia (Lazy eye), 4,
    11, 16, 19, 74, 134 137, 141,
    143, 146, 148, 150. *See* also
    Strabismus
Asthenopia, 97, 98, 111, 116, 117
Astigmatism, 141
Attention Deficit Disorders
    (ADD/ADHD), 34, 137, 141
Aviation, 60, 63, 121, 122

Barry, Susan, xiii, 7, 10, 17,
    81–83, 87, 103, 105, 106, 119,
    128, 139, 147, 149
Battle for the middle, 20, 30,
    40, 45, 62, 111
Behavioral issues/Acting out,
    5, 34, 51, 58

Behavioral/Developmental
    Optometry, xi, 129, 130,
    132, 142
Binocular Vision, 4, 10, 18, 34,
    54, 55, 62, 75, 76, 79, 110,
    139, 141, 144, 145
Blind spot, 31, 63, 142
Boatbuilding, 65–69
Botulinum toxin injection, 133
Brain, xii, xiii, 3–6, 10, 11, 14,
    15, 18–20, 29, 31, 32, 35, 39,
    41, 44, 45, 47, 62, 65, 74,
    75, 77, 78, 84, 86, 90, 93,
    99–102, 110, 112, 113, 116,
    118, 126, 131, 133, 134, 139,
    142, 143, 146, 147
Brock string, 55, 84, 89, 91, 113

Cessna, 61, 122
Concord, Massachusetts, 13,
    22, 27, 49, 52, 53, 60
Convergence, 10, 62, 146
Cornea, 142
Cosmetic surgery, 27, 80, 130,
    133

Critical period, ix, 6, 17, 21, 55, 99, 119, 127, 128, 142

Crockett, James Underwood, and *Crockett's Victory Garden*, 13, 23, 65

Cross-eyed, x, 3, 4, 9, 19, 27, 54, 75 76, 79, 117. *See* also Strabismus

Depth perception, 19, 21

Diplopia, 77, 142

Distance perception, 19, 41, 48, 62, 77

Dobson, Angela, x, xi, 6, 83–85, 91, 96, 115, 127, 139, 147, 149

Doidge, Norman, 99, 100, 110, 147

Dominant eye, xi, 11, 29, 47, 68, 74–76, 89, 93, 102, 112

Double images, 14, 20, 74–78, 94, 96, 97, 112, 142

Dyslexia, 34, 137

Eye muscles, 4, 9, 10, 14, 75, 90, 101, 119, 129–134, 147

Eye operation. *See* Surgery (eye)

Fair Wind and Plenty of It, 71

Feldenkrais Method, 101, 149

Field of vision, 20, 41

Fixing My Gaze, ix, xiii, 10, 81, 82, 103, 128, 147. *See* also Barry, Susan

Floating third eye, 75, 113. *See* also Vision Problems

Fresnel lenses, 95

Fusion, 10 16, 55, 96, 107, 109, 110, 114, 117, 128, 134, 144

Gallop, Steven, 1, 119, 130, 137, 140, 147, 150

Halifax. *See* Nova Scotia

Harvard Divinity School, 21

Hubel, David, 119, 128

Jump duction, 116, 117, 120

Lazy eye. *See* Amblyopia

Lewis, Robin, 18, 115, 117, 139 149

Lunenburg. *See* Nova Scotia

MacDonald, Lawrence OD, 54, 77, 140, 147

Marsden ball, 87

Massachusetts, 13, 52, 58, 60, 119

Monocular vision, 12, 16, 18, 74, 116

Motion parallax, 19, 62

Near-sighted, 11

Neuron, 10, 100, 101, 104, 143

Neuroplasticity, 34, 99, 100, 119, 143, 147

Non-dominant eye, xi, 74, 76, 89, 93

Non-invasive methods, 4, 8, 15

Nova Scotia, 66, 67, 70, 82, 115, 118, 121, 140, 147

Occlusion, 143, 144

Ophthalmologists, 15, 89, 100, 128

Ophthamology, 143

Optician, 143

Optometrists, x, xi, 6, 7, 15, 54, 55, 82–84, 89, 90, 100, 115, 116, 120, 129, 130, 132, 144, 149

Optometry, xi, 142, 144, 149

Panorama, 20, 62, 115, 117, 118

Patch (eye), 89, 143, 144

Pathways, 10, 100–102, 143

Perception, 19, 21, 41, 48, 62, 77, 78, 113, 141, 144

Peripheral vision, 18, 20, 29, 47, 48, 74, 93, 98, 116, 134, 144

Perspective, 19, 47, 70, 116, 119, 126, 132

Picton Castle, 70

Posterior Vitreous Detachment, 57

Prism, 90, 94, 95, 116, 117, 120, 142, 144, 146

Proprioception, 111

Retina, 56, 57, 74, 76, 142, 144

Rose Bay Boat Shop. *See* Boatbuilding

Ruggiero, Theresa, 120, 140, 148

Sacks, Oliver, ix, 7, 81, 148

Sensory fusion, 144

Sorkin, Richard, 55, 56, 140, 150

Stereo Sue. *See* Barry, Susan

Stereoblindness, ix, 4, 5, 16, 18, 19, 41, 45, 47, 55, 68, 76, 108, 126

Stereopsis, xii, xiii, 6, 18, 19, 21, 55, 89, 100, 103, 105, 108–110, 113, 114, 120, 128, 144

Stereoscopic Vision. *See* 3D Vision

Strabismus, (squint, tropia, crossed eyes, wall eyes) x, xi, 3, 4, 11, 14–16, 28, 40, 55, 56, 76, 79, 81, 82, 84, 89, 101, 103, 119, 126, 128, 129, 130, 132, 145–147, 150

Infantile, 11, 16, 128

Suppression, ix, xi, xii 11, 29, 31, 35, 41, 47, 59, 63, 75–77, 86, 90, 93, 95, 99, 102, 109, 141, 145

Surgery (eye), 3–7, 14–16, 21, 27, 29, 35, 75, 80, 81, 101, 119, 128–134, 143, 147

Symptoms, 34, 56, 135, 141, 146

Syntonics, 87, 120, 142, 144, 149

Torticollis, 145

Transcendentalism (Emerson, Hawthorne, Thoreau, Alcott, French), 52, 53

Trauma, 3, 5, 7, 11, 15, 82, 101, 129, 146

University of Massachusetts, 58, 60

Vanderhoof Hardware, 43, 44, 140

Vergara Gimnez, Pilar, 16, 134, 135, 140, 146, 148, 150

Vision,
    Challenges, 5, 37, 59
    Exercises, 15
    Problems, 5, 6, 33, 34, 41, 45, 51 72, 129, 135, 146

Vision Sense. *See* Dobson, Angela

Vision therapy and training, ix, xi-xiii, 4, 6, 7, 14–16, 48, 54, 76, 82–84, 89, 90, 94, 97, 98, 100, 101, 103, 106, 115, 117–119, 129, 130, 133, 134, 144, 146, 147, 148, 150

Visual acuity, 34, 40, 77, 79, 141, 145

Visual Confusion, 145

Visual cortex, 146

Visual impairment, 48, 57

Vitreous humor, 57

Wall-eyed. *See* Strabismus

Williams, Margaret-Ellen, 13

36443599R00104